HEALTH & SAFETY IN
ROOF WORK

HSG33

HSE BOOKS

First published 1998
Reprinted 1999, 2002, 2004

ISBN 0 7176 1425 5

This guidance is issued by the Health and Safety Executive.
Following the guidance is not compulsory and you are free to
take other action. But if you do follow the guidance you will
normally be doing enough to comply with the law. Health and
safety inspectors seek to secure compliance with the law and
may refer to this guidance as illustrating good practice.

Contents

Preface

Every year many construction site workers are killed or injured as a result of their work, and others suffer ill health. The hazards are not, however, restricted to those working on sites. Children and other members of the public are also killed or injured because construction activities have not been adequately controlled. The construction industry's performance has improved over the past decade, but the rates of death, serious injury and ill health are still too high.

These deaths, injuries and ill health cause pain and suffering; they also cost money. A recent HSE survey found that 8.5% of the tender price could have been saved, even on a site which had no serious (reportable) injuries.

This booklet is part of HSE's revised series of health and safety guidance for construction.

The series will be developed over the next few years. The aim of the series is to help all those involved in construction to identify the main causes of accidents and ill health and to explain how to eliminate the hazards and control the risks. The guidance is simple. It will refer to other relevant documents so that you can build up a clear and comprehensive package.

Each piece of guidance will have general relevance to everyone involved in the construction process, from clients and designers, to contractors and individual workers. But some documents will be particularly relevant to particular groups, depending on the subject they address. All the new guidance will be identified with this logo.

Introduction

Why is this guidance needed?

1   Roof work is dangerous. Almost one in five construction deaths are caused by falls from or through roofs. Falls through fragile materials such as roof lights and asbestos cement roofing sheets account for more of these deaths than any other single cause. There are also many serious injuries, often resulting in permanent disabilities. These accidents occur across the whole range of roof work from the simplest repairs to large-scale construction projects (see Figure 1).

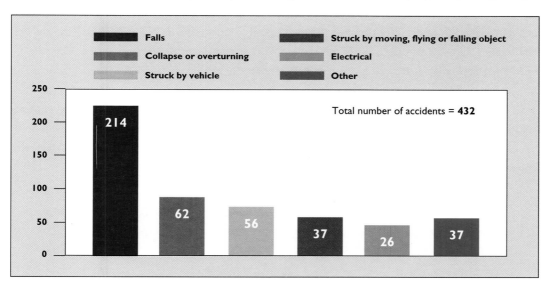

Figure 1(a) *Falls are the biggest killer in construction*

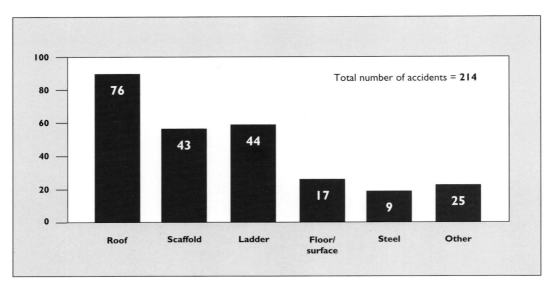

Figure 1(b) *Most fatal falls are from roofs*

What is this book about?

2   This book gives guidance on how to work safely on roofs and how to design and plan for safe working. It covers new buildings, repair, maintenance, cleaning work and demolition. It also gives guidance for those not directly involved in work on the roof, eg clients, designers and specifiers. Clients should provide adequate resources in terms of time and money so that the work can be carried out safely. They can benefit from reduced running costs if maintenance and repair are considered early in the design process.

3   Designers need to take account of the health and safety implications of their decisions. They can often make risks disappear by designing them out at source. Designers need to understand the problems faced by contractors to realise these benefits. If not, they could be breaking the law as well as helping to perpetuate one of the biggest workplace killers. Margin highlighted with a light tint ▢, shows that nearby text is particularly relevant to designers (see left hand margin).

4   The principal problems are falls through fragile roofing materials and falls from unprotected roof edges. In most cases, straightforward physical protection measures can prevent accidents occurring. Accidents can usually be prevented. But too often a lack of foresight and management control means the necessary protection is neglected during high-risk work.

> *An 18-year-old labourer was helping to carry roof sheets from a stack on another part of the roof to the working position. He slipped from a single staging placed over a partially fixed GRP (glass reinforced plastic) roof light. He fell between the staging and the edge of the roof light, which tore from its fixings. He fell 10.5 m to his death.*

> *A foreman carrying out work on a roof parapet suffered brain damage when he fell through a PVC (polyvinyl chloride) roof light during a refurbishment project. The roof light had been painted to reduce glare in the building. This made it very difficult to distinguish the roof lights from the metal top sheets. None of the many hundreds of roof lights on the building had been protected, in spite of the fact that work was carried out close to them.*

5   Not all the safeguards in this guidance will be relevant in all circumstances. What is needed depends on the extent and nature of the risks. The guidance is structured to identify precautions that are applicable to all roof work. It also includes those which are particularly relevant to different types of roof and different types of work. However, risks are significant in **all** roof work and high standards are necessary to provide adequate protection.

Who should read this book?

6   Roof work is not just an issue for construction companies. Non-construction workers such as factory maintenance staff are often involved in falls from or through roofs. This guidance will be useful to:

- directors and partners of companies who carry out roof work;
- clients of projects involving roof work;
- designers and specifiers of buildings and components;
- planning supervisors;
- principal contractors for projects which include roof work;
- trade union safety representatives and employees' safety representatives;
- anyone carrying out roof work, including employees and the self-employed;
- safety consultants and advisers.

Other useful information sources

7   This book does not repeat detailed guidance available about other topics or equipment common to construction work in general, eg access scaffolds, mobile access equipment, hoists, etc. The Reference section gives a list of useful publications and indicates where such advice can be found.

The law

8   A range of law is relevant to roof work safety. The principal elements are:

- The Health and Safety at Work etc Act 1974;

- The Management of Health and Safety at Work Regulations 1999;
- The Construction (Health Safety and Welfare) Regulations 1996;
- The Construction (Design and Management) Regulations 1994; and
- The Lifting Operations and Lifting Equipment Regulations 1998.

HSE guidance *Health and safety in construction* HSG150 contains more detailed information on these legal requirements.[1]

Working safely: general issues

Safe place of work on the roof

9   For all roof work, whatever its nature or extent, a safe place of work should be provided.

10   Safety method statements should identify working positions, access routes **to** the roof and **on** the roof and show:

- how falls are to be prevented;
- how danger to those at work below and to the public from falling materials is to be controlled;
- how risks to health will be controlled;
- how other risks, identified at planning and survey stages, are to be controlled, for example handling hot bitumen;
- what equipment will be needed;
- what competence/training is needed;
- who will supervise the job 'on site';
- how changes in the work will be dealt with without prejudicing safe working; and
- who will check that the system is effectively controlling risk.

(See Appendix 1 for further information.)

11   There is a hierarchy of different safeguards. If work at height cannot be avoided, the most effective precaution is to provide a safe place of work. This can be in the form of a safe working

platform with physical safeguards such as guard rails, toe boards, and barriers. This protects everyone on the platform and does not rely on people following a system of work or using special equipment which needs training to be effective. Only if this first level of protection cannot be achieved in practice are lower levels such as fall arrest systems acceptable.

12   Fall arrest systems do not prevent falls, but can reduce injury once a fall has happened. There are two basic types.

- Those that give general protection, eg safety nets.
- Those giving individual protection, eg safety harness attached to a suitable anchorage point.

> **All fall arrest systems must be properly installed and maintained by a competent person** (see Appendices 2 and 3 for further information).

13   Safety nets, once properly rigged, can protect everyone within the area of the net. They also allow maximum freedom of movement on the roof. They should be installed as close as possible beneath the working position to reduce the potential fall distance. They are particularly suited to open span structures such as portal frame buildings with minimum obstructions.

14   Harnesses need to be suitable for the individual, who should be trained to fit and use them. They only protect an individual when they are used **and** when properly fitted **and** only while they are attached to a suitable anchorage point. There must be enough clear space below the work position to allow the fall to be arrested safely (see Appendix 3). In order to avoid serious injury, you should check the supplier's recommendations about the maximum time interval before rescue is completed (see paragraph 133). Such systems need active and effective management to ensure they are properly and consistently implemented. They are not an easy option.

Safe access to the roof

15   This requires careful planning particularly where work progresses along the roof. Typical methods are:

- independent scaffolds;
- fixed or mobile scaffold towers;
- mobile access equipment;
- ladders.

More detailed advice on the selection and use of access equipment is given in the HSE publication *Health and safety in construction* HSG150.[1]

Independent scaffold

16   An independent scaffold can provide safe access to roof level, and also access around the edge of the roof and materials storage space. A loading bay can often be provided and can greatly simplify materials handling on the roof.

17   On sites where people from more than one trade are working, the principal contractor and the roofing contractor should agree what is necessary and who will provide it. They should also agree who will carry out the necessary statutory inspections. All employers need to ensure that scaffolds are suitable and safe before being used by their employees.

Tower scaffolds

18   These can provide safe access, provided that they are erected by a competent person and used correctly. 'Stairway' designs are preferable to ladders as they allow materials such as small components or tools to be safely carried onto the roof (see Figure 2).

Mobile access equipment

19   A wide range of this equipment is available. For work of short duration, such as inspection and minor maintenance, it can provide excellent safe access to the roof. Risks associated with scaffold erection can often be avoided if mobile access equipment is used rather than scaffolding. However, the equipment chosen should be appropriate for the ground conditions on the site. The manufacturer's advice on the maximum wind speed at which it can be safely operated should be followed. Equipment should be maintained in a safe condition and be operated only by competent personnel.

Figure 2   Tower scaffolds can provide good access. Make sure they are properly secured

Ladders

20   Ladders may provide safe access, but their use is not always appropriate. Factors to be considered include:

- the length of the ladder required. Very long ladders are heavy to handle and may need staying to reduce flexing in use;
- the need to carry materials, small components, tools, etc. Both hands should be free when climbing a ladder.

21   When ladders are used, they need to be of the right type, ie a suitable grade of industrial ladder. They should be in good condition and effectively secured to prevent movement. Permanent means of securing ladders at identified access points can improve ladder safety. This avoids the need for footing when ladders are tied and untied. Those who use, inspect and secure ladders should be competent to do so.

> *A 39-year-old labourer fell over 4 m from a ladder onto concrete while attempting to replace four roof tiles as part of the renovation of council houses. The ladder was erected on the flat roof of an outhouse. It was not tied, footed or secured in any way. His skull was fractured and he died ten days later.*

Escape in case of fire

22   You should also consider how to escape from the roof in case of fire. A fire could result from:

- construction work on a roof, eg welding or hot work using bitumen; or
- activities inside a building including those under refurbishment.

23   In either case the means of escape must be adequate. How complex this needs to be depends on the risk of being trapped if there is a fire. It could mean, for example, ensuring that mobile access equipment is always available in case of an emergency, or the provision of additional (tied) ladders. Further guidance is given in HSE booklet *Fire safety in construction work* HSG168.[2]

Materials handling

24   Well planned materials handling has a significant impact on roofwork safety. For example it can:

- minimise the amount of time spent working at height;

- reduce the amount of travelling around the roof to collect materials;
- reduce injuries caused by handling heavy and unwieldy components, eg roof trusses.

It can also increase productivity and reduce waste.

25   Designers should consider reducing the length of roof sheets. This makes the sheets lighter and also reduces the risk of excess wind loading when handled at height. These advantages should be considered alongside the need to minimise maintenance work on the roof (see paragraph 200).

A member of the public was seriously injured when hit by tiles thrown from a roof while it was being stripped. The use of a waste chute would have prevented the accident (see Figure 3).

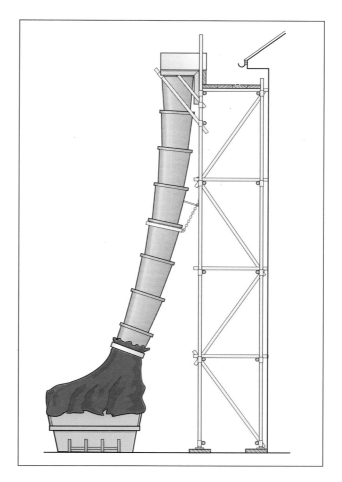

Figure 3   *Waste chutes make waste handling easier and safer*

Mechanical handling

26   General guidance on the siting and operation of cranes is given in British Standard 7121 *Code of practice for safe use of cranes.*[3] Sufficient resources should be allowed to ensure that cranes or other mechanical handling devices are available when needed.

27   Where small lifting appliances such as a gin wheel, gantry hoist or scaffold hoist are mounted near the edge of a roof, suitable guard rails and toe boards should be installed. This safeguards those using the appliance from falling.

28   Lifting appliances of this type need a secure anchorage. When counterweights are used they must be adequate to allow a safety factor of not less than three. If the lifting appliance is a gin wheel, you should allow for the force exerted by the person who is raising the load (see Figures 4(a) and 4(b)).

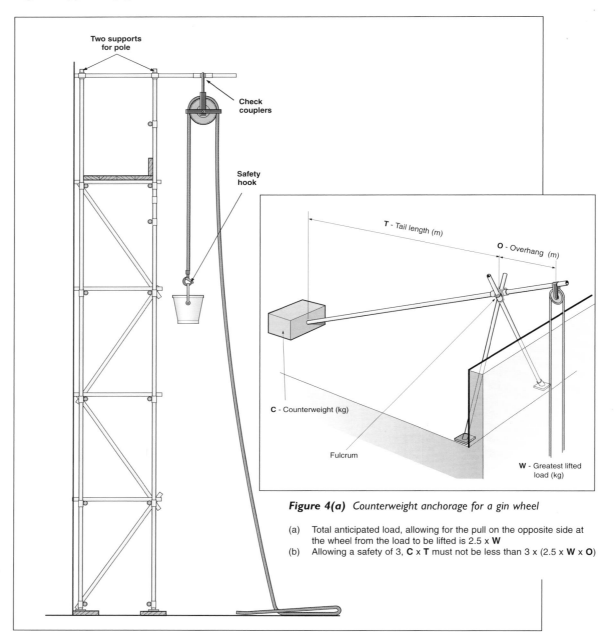

Figure 4(a) *Counterweight anchorage for a gin wheel*

(a)   Total anticipated load, allowing for the pull on the opposite side at the wheel from the load to be lifted is 2.5 x **W**

(b)   Allowing a safety of 3, **C** x **T** must not be less than 3 x (2.5 x **W** x **O**)

Figure 4(b) *Properly erected gin wheel*

29   Counterweights should be secured to the tail of the appliance to prevent removal or interference. Rolls of felt, blocks of bitumen, etc, which are liable to be removed and used in the roofing operation, should be avoided.

30 Where practicable, guard rails and toe boards should be maintained in position when material is being raised or lowered. If, unusually, they have to be removed, any person who needs to be near the edge, eg signalling or to assist in moving the load, should wear a safety harness attached to a suitable anchorage point (see Appendix 3).

31 All hooks used in lifting operations should be fitted with safety catches.

32 Every lifting appliance should be properly installed, maintained and inspected and operated at all times within its safe working load. All lifting appliances need a periodic thorough inspection.[1]

33 Access to the area below a lifting point should be controlled, eg by temporary fencing.

Falling materials

34 The public as well as other workers can be at risk when materials fall from roofs. These include roof sheets, fixings, tools, roof tiles, roofing felt and hot bitumen. Controlling risk to the public is discussed in paragraphs 141-146. Many of the measures described will also be required to protect people at work.

35 Access by other trades needs to be controlled when roof workers are working overhead and there is risk of falling materials. This should be considered in the programming of overlapping work packages. Where work is carried out below roof workers, effective measures will be required to prevent injury, such as the provision of a birdcage scaffold or suitable debris netting (see Figure 5).

Figure 5   *Debris netting used in addition to safety netting may enable work to be carried out safely below roof workers*

A client (a major supermarket chain) identified and provided additional resources for the installation of safety nets and debris netting during the roofing phase of a new 'superstore'. This allowed the roof workers to work quickly and safely within the protection of the nets. The addition of debris netting also allowed work to be carried out below them as the risk from falling materials was controlled. As a result, delays were minimised and savings were made on labour costs.

Weather conditions

36   Adverse weather conditions need to be anticipated and suitable precautions taken. Rain, ice or snow can turn a secure footing into a skating rink. A roof should always be inspected before work starts to see if conditions have changed and to check whether it is safe to work.

37   A sudden gust of wind can lead to loss of balance. Roof sheets and, in some circumstances, roofing felt should not be fixed in windy weather as people can easily be thrown off balance while carrying a sheet up to or on the roof.

38   When deciding whether to continue or suspend work consider:

•   wind speed;
•   the measures which have already been taken to prevent falls from the roof;
•   the position and height of the roof and the size of the material being handled.

An anenometer should be available to measure wind speed on the roof if large sheets are being handled (see Figure 6).

39   Guidance on work in windy conditions has been published by the National Federation of Roofing Contractors.[5] This includes recommended maximum wind speeds for particular operations.

Figure 6   *Using a simple anemometer to check wind speed at roof level*

40   Sites should be inspected at the end of the working day to ensure that loose materials, especially sheets, offcuts and fixings, are not left on the roof.

Electricity at work

41   If there are overhead electric lines crossing the site or near the site, there may be danger of contact or near contact with, for example, scaffold tubes, metal roof sheets or ladders, causing flashover.

42   Designers need to consider changing the footprint of the building or relocating lines to eliminate the risk of contact during construction and maintenance. Where roof workers have to work near overhead lines, designers should also review the length of metal roof sheets and any other long conducting objects such as metal finishing strips. Principal contractors should consider applying for power to be switched off or arranging for protection (sheathing) of cables to control any residual risk.

> *A roof worker was electrocuted when moving an aluminium ladder which contacted an 11 kV power line. He was repairing storm damage to the roof. The power lines ran parallel to the eaves, less than 2 m away.*

> *During the construction of a steel framed agricultural building, a building worker was modifying the scaffold tube roof edge protection at the gable end. The 7.5 m scaffold tube was unclamped and turned through 180° in order to pass it down. The tube contacted an 11 kV overhead power line, killing the labourer.*

43   Use of portable electrical tools can create hazards. For example, metal roof sheet edges can damage cable insulation. All electrical supplies to portable tools should be obtained from properly constructed and installed plugs and sockets of the industrial type. Where possible, battery operated tools should be used. If this is not practicable, a reduced low voltage system, sometimes referred to as 110 volt centre tapped to earth (CTE) system should be used. All electrical equipment should be properly installed and maintained (see *Electrical safety on construction sites* HSG141[6] and BS 7375 : 1996[7]).

Types of work

44   This section considers the different safeguards which can be required in different types of roof work.

Inspection

45   Inspection of roofs, eg prior to refurbishment, must be done with care, by those trained and experienced in assessing the risks involved. Preferably, the work should be carried out from a safe place. This could be from an adjacent structure, using binoculars or from mobile access equipment or a secured ladder. Some investigations can be carried out from below if the roof structure is exposed. If inspectors cannot avoid going onto a roof, they will be exposed to high risks, and high safety standards will be required (see Figure 7).

> **All roof work is potentially dangerous however short-lived.**

> *A self-employed roofing contractor died after falling 15 m while surveying a flat roof on a hotel. No consideration had been given to providing safe means of access.*

A quality assurance manager was carrying out an inspection of a completed re-roof of an industrial building. He fell 7 m from the roof edge suffering fatal injuries. No risk assessment had been carried out, and his employer had no system for carrying out this type of work safely.

Refurbishment

46   Roof refurbishment can be complex, is always high risk and demands careful planning. For example:

- any fragile elements in the roof, such as cement sheets, glazing, plastic roof lights or wood wool slabs, should be clearly identified as early as possible (see paragraphs 96-108 and Appendix 4);
- the precautions to prevent people falling through fragile parts of the roof should be clearly identified. These need not always be complex, but must be effective. They include the protection of people who work on **or** pass by fragile material;
- close liaison with the client will be necessary where premises remain occupied during refurbishment;
- a structural survey may be required to confirm the strength or stability of roof members;
- a risk assessment should be carried out when deciding whether to refurbish or to replace fragile roof coverings. For example, the decision on whether to clean and seal or replace an existing asbestos cement roof should take into account the additional risks and cost of future maintenance (see paragraph 156). Where cleaning is carried out, a safe system must be adopted (see paragraph 109-118).

See also paragraphs 34 and 142.

Maintenance and cleaning

47   Many accidents occur during maintenance and cleaning of roofs. Often little attention is paid to this short-term, low value work. It is often done by those with no experience in, or aptitude for, work at height.

48   A high proportion of deaths are caused by falls through fragile materials. Any work on fragile roofs, however trivial it may seem, should be carefully assessed, planned and supervised. Factors to be taken into account when assessing the risk include:

- roof lights which may have been obscured by paint;
- any repairs carried out in the past, especially if fragile roof sheets have been used for 'patching' an otherwise non-fragile roof. Such practices are highly dangerous;

- metal roof sheets which may have deteriorated with age and become fragile;
- wood wool slabs which may have been weakened by water damage.

See paragraphs 96-118.

49   A good survey, together with local knowledge, will help to identify such problems. In case of doubt the roof should be assumed to be fragile. The precautions described for working on or near fragile materials should be rigorously followed, whatever the size of the job.

Figure 7   *Powered access for the inspection of a large fragile roof*

50   A typical example is the cleaning of valley gutters on an asbestos cement roof or a roof containing fragile roof lights. Systems are available to provide long-term protection for these regular operations, and should be considered for existing roofs, see Figure 24. The alternative is to provide extensive temporary protection for each operation. This can be less cost-effective and its use requires rigorous supervision (see Figure 8).

A foreman was cleaning cement dust which had spilled from a silo vent when he fell 3.5 m through an asbestos cement roof. He was walking down the valley gutter which was 300 mm wide. No protection was provided for fragile material and no other precautions were taken to prevent falls. He died from head injuries.

Figure 8   *Access system for short-term maintenance work on a fragile roof*

Stripping and dismantling of roofs

51   Stripping roofs to reclaim tiles and timber during demolition have often involved unsafe practices. An independent scaffold should be provided at eaves level. This gives safe access to the roof, and room for storage of materials. The scaffolding contractor should be informed of the intended loading and care must be taken not to exceed this. It may be necessary to give specific guidance to site supervisors on the maximum number of tiles or slates per scaffold bay.

52   Timber battens deteriorate with age. They should **not** be used as footholds unless they have been inspected by a competent person to confirm that they have sufficient residual strength.

53   As the roof is stripped, steps must be taken to prevent internal falls, for example through the roof joists. The best option is often the use of mobile access equipment, provided that ground conditions are suitable. Harnesses are only appropriate where safe anchorage points are available and there is sufficient space clear of obstructions below the working position (see Appendix 3 for further advice).

> *A teenager fell 10 m to his death while removing slates from a roof. The slates were being reclaimed prior to demolition. They were stored on a small area of flat roof adjacent to the pitched roof. He was loading the slates onto an inclined hoist when he fell. No edge protection was provided at the flat roof.*

> *A demolition foreman was removing asbestos cement roof sheets from a factory roof when he fell 7.5 m through the fragile roof to the concrete floor below. He received multiple injuries from which he died four weeks later. No equipment was provided on the roof to allow the work to be carried out safely.*

54   Mechanical handling devices and waste chutes are particularly relevant to demolition where large quantities of waste and reclaimed materials are removed from roofs.

55   Demolition of buildings with fragile roof sheets or liners requires careful planning. The Construction (Design and Management) Regulations 1994 (CDM) require that all those (including clients) who appoint contractors are satisfied that they have the necessary competence and resources. **Resources include the time needed to plan and carry out the work safely.**

56   Asbestos cement sheet is a fragile material and cannot be relied upon to support the weight of a person. If the asbestos cement sheets are in good condition and it is possible to provide safe access, preferably from underneath (using, eg scissors lifts), then the sheets should be taken down whole. If using this method, the sheets should not be dropped or damaged. They are best disposed of by careful transfer to covered vehicles or skips, or by wrapping intact in heavy duty sheet plastic. For advice on waste disposal read *Special waste regulations: how they affect you*.[8]

57   If the roofing sheets are in poor condition, ie liable to break when handled, or if safe access cannot be provided and the risk of falling is too great, then remote demolition is preferred. This could be by machine, such as a pusher arm or deliberate controlled collapse. In this case the precautions outlined in Appendix 5 to control the spread of asbestos should be observed.

Short duration work

58   For work of short duration (taking minutes rather than hours) it may not be reasonably practicable to install safeguards such as edge protection. The decision on the precautions to be taken will depend on an overall assessment of the risks involved which should consider:

- duration of the work;
- complexity of the work;
- pitch of the roof;
- condition of the roof;
- weather conditions;
- risk to those putting up edge protection;
- risk to other workers and the public.

59   Mobile access equipment can provide a safe working platform in some situations (see Figure 9). Where this is not practicable, then travel restraint or fall arrest should be considered.

Figure 9   *Simple mobile access used for short-term work at gutter level*

60   Travel restraint can prevent a fall by physically restricting the movement of a person to a safe area. It should not be possible to reach any unprotected edge, hole or fragile material when relying on this system.

Fall arrest is not the same as travel restraint (see Figure 10). Fall arrest relies on minimising injury once a fall has occurred. In both cases, specialist advice should be sought from the supplier of the equipment on anchorage points. Supervision and training are needed to ensure that the system of work adopted is understood by all and is maintained. See Appendices 2 and 3 for further information on fall arrest.

Figure 10   *Fall arrest used during short-term inspection of a flat roof. If the surveyor falls, an inertia reel device will arrest his fall. Longer term work involving approach to the edge would require proper edge protection.*

Types of roof

61   This section explains the hazards characteristic of different roof types and the precautionary measures required to deal with them.

Flat roofs

62   On flat roofs, falls most frequently occur:

*   from the edge of a completed roof;
*   from the edge where work is being carried out;
*   through openings or gaps;
*   through fragile material.

63   Where the design of the roof does not provide permanent edge protection, then temporary edge protection will normally be required, eg by means of guard rails and toe boards which should when erected:

*   give protection during the full course of the work;
*   be strong and rigid enough to prevent people from falling and be able to withstand other loads likely to be placed on them;
*   when fixed to a structure this should be capable of supporting them; and
*   be designed in such a way that it is not necessary to remove them in order to work at the edge of the roof (see Figure 11).

Figure 11   *Temporary flat roof edge protection. Adjustable supports enable work to progress with protection in place*

64   Guard rails should preferably be supported at ground level, if the height of the building allows, as they will then create no obstructions to work on the roof (see Figure 12). For a higher structure, they can be supported by an upstand at the edge of the roof, if this has adequate strength (see Figure 13). Guard rails can also be supported by frames, counterweights or scaffolding on the roof.

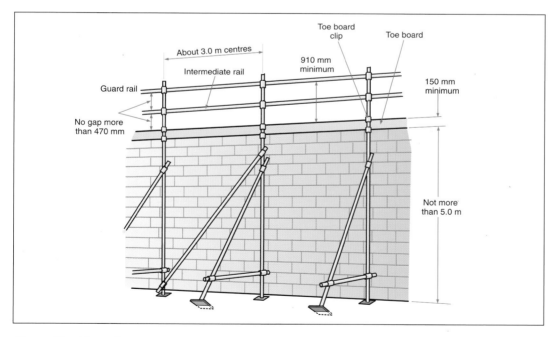

Figure 12   *Flat roof edge protection supported at ground level. Ground level support allows work up to the roof edge without obstruction*

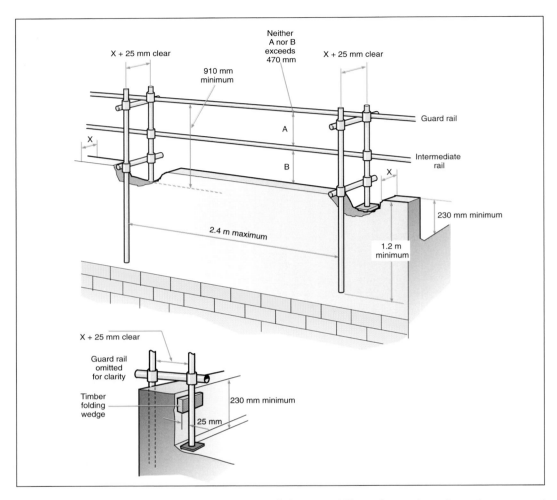

Figure 13   *Flat roof edge protection supported on the roof edge upstand. The roof upstand must have adequate strength*

65   All guard rails should meet the minimum legal standard, ie they should include:

*   a main guard rail at least 910 mm above any edge from which people are liable to fall;
*   a toe board at least 150 mm high; and
*   an intermediate guard rail, barrier or suitable alternative, positioned so that the unprotected gap is no greater than 470 mm.

Demarcation of access routes and work areas on flat roofs

66   Where limited work is being carried out on sections of a large roof, a simple form of barrier some distance from the roof edge could identify the work area and any access route to it. The distance should be adequate to ensure that people working within the demarcated area **cannot** fall from the edge of the roof. For roofs with a slight slope where this method is used, it may be necessary to prevent materials rolling away, beyond the 'safe' area.

67   In most circumstances a distance of at least 2 m from the edge will be sufficient. This will depend on the geometry of the roof and may need to be increased. This type of barrier is only acceptable where there is a high level of supervision and discipline to ensure that people do not go beyond the demarcated area. There should be no unprotected holes, breaks or fragile material within the 'safe area'. Barriers should be sufficiently durable and be immediately obvious to all. Markings at foot level are not a suitable alternative to a barrier (see Figure 14).

Figure 14   Demarcation barriers on a large non-fragile roof, preventing access to the adjacent fragile roof lights. The roof lights are at least 2 m from the barrier

68   For short duration work on flat roofs, it may not be feasible to provide edge protection (see paragraphs 58-60).

Sloping roofs

69   On traditional pitched roofs, most falls occur:

- from the eaves;
- from the roof, typically slipping down the roof, then falling from the eaves;
- from the roof, falling internally, for example during roof truss erection or demolition (stripping) of roofs;
- from gable ends.

70   Falls from sloping roofs are more likely if the pitch is steep, if the surface is slippery and in windy conditions. Moisture, ice, snow, moss and lichens all increase the risk of slipping. See paragraphs 36-40.

71   For work on sloping roofs, unless of very short duration, full edge protection is required on all roof elevations to which access is needed. This is to prevent people and materials falling from the lower edge of the roof. The potential loading on edge protection when a person slides down a pitched roof onto it is much greater compared to falling against it on a flat roof. Make sure that the scaffold supplier knows the roof pitch when specifying edge protection.

72   If work on the roof requires access within 2 m of gable ends, then edge protection will be needed at those edges.

73   A scaffold platform at eaves level provides a good standard of edge protection, a working platform and storage space for materials. Brick guards will be necessary if materials, eg roof slates are stacked above toe board height. They also reduce gaps between guard rails but need to be designed for this purpose, taking account of the pitch of the roof, and to be securely fixed (see Figure 15).

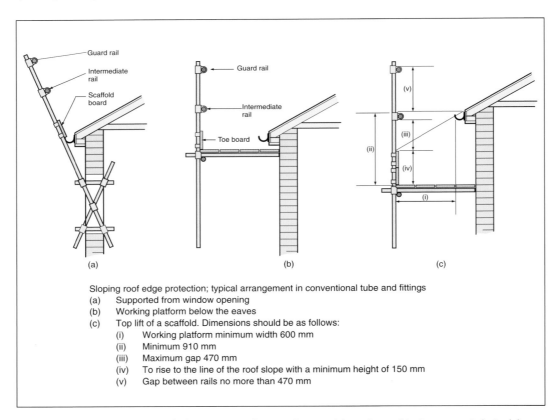

Sloping roof edge protection; typical arrangement in conventional tube and fittings
(a)   Supported from window opening
(b)   Working platform below the eaves
(c)   Top lift of a scaffold. Dimensions should be as follows:
    (i)   Working platform minimum width 600 mm
    (ii)   Minimum 910 mm
    (iii) Maximum gap 470 mm
    (iv)   To rise to the line of the roof slope with a minimum height of 150 mm
    (v)   Gap between rails no more than 470 mm

Figure 15   *Typical sloping roof edge protection. Barriers shown in (a) can be useful where space is limited, but they are not capable of sustaining loads so large as (b) and (c) which also provide a working platform*

74   Where independent scaffold edge protection is not reasonably practicable, barriers can be attached to the structure instead. Barriers must be high enough and strong enough to stop a person who is rolling or sliding down a roof slope (see Figure 15).

75   With some long, steeply sloping roofs, edge protection may prevent a fall from eaves level. But it may not prevent serious injury if a roof worker falls from a position high on the roof slope. Additional precautions may be required, eg work platforms cantilevered out from an independent scaffold. If this is not practicable, then safety harnesses may be appropriate (see Appendix 3). In all cases, the edge protection should be designed to minimise injury as well as to prevent a further fall. Safety netting can be incorporated into edge protection to absorb some of the energy of impact. However, netting on its own is no substitute for appropriate edge protection.

76   For work of short duration on a pitched roof (eg replacing a few tiles or slates) the decision on whether or not to erect edge protection will depend on a number of factors (see paragraphs 58-60).

77   The minimum standard for such short duration work on a pitched roof is:

- safe means of access to roof level;
- a properly constructed and supported roof ladder (see below) or equivalent .

Roof workers should **not** work directly on tiles or slates unless additional measures to prevent falls, eg a safety harness with a suitable anchorage point, are provided.

78   For work on chimneys, a properly designed chimney scaffold should be used (see Figures 16(a) and 16(b)).

Figure 16(a)   *A traditional chimney scaffold*

Figure 16(b)   *Proprietary system for access to roof and chimney*

Roof ladders

79   On most sloping roofs, suitable roof ladders or crawling boards will be essential, **in addition to** edge protection. Where a high standard of edge protection is provided, it **may** be safe to work without a roof ladder. This may apply if the pitch is shallow and the surface provides particularly good foothold. The decision in each case should be based on a risk assessment.

80   Roof ladders or crawling boards should be:

- designed and fabricated to be fit for purpose;
- strong enough to support workers when spanning across the supports for the roof covering;
- long enough to span the supports (at least three rafters);
- secured or placed to prevent accidental movement.

81   The anchorage at the top of the roof ladder should be by some method which does not depend on the ridge capping. This is liable to break away from the ridge. The anchorage should bear on the opposite slope by a properly designed and manufactured ridge iron or be secured by other means (see Figure 17).

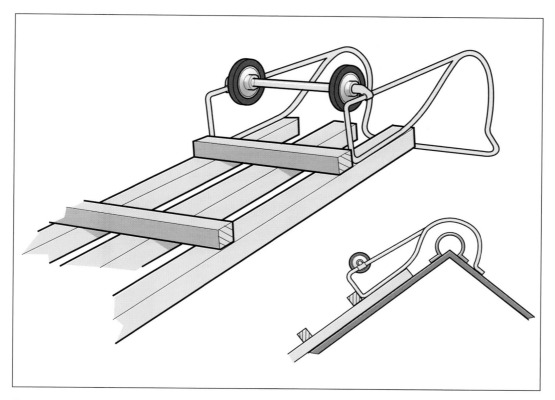

Figure 17   *Roof ladder. The ridge iron should be large enough to be clear of the ridge tile*

82   Eaves gutters should not be used as a footing or to support a roof ladder unless they are of adequate strength. This is not usually the case. Gutters normally used on houses are not suitable.

83   As an alternative to roof ladders, timber battens used for slated and tiled roofs can provide a reasonably secure foothold provided that:

*   they are of good quality;
*   they are fixed to rafters not more than 450 mm apart;
*   they meet BS 5534 Part 1 minimum standard.[10]

84   The amount battens project above the rafters or the type of weather sheeting, eg felting, alters the security of the foothold.

85   The age and consequential weakening of exposed battens should be investigated before they are used for footholds.

86   A roof ladder will always be required at some stage, eg towards the end of the job when the battens are covered by tiles.

A self-employed builder was killed when he fell from a domestic roof. He was reducing and re-pointing a chimney stack. He was using a home-made roof ladder which was in poor condition. A properly designed and erected chimney scaffold would have prevented the accident.

A self-employed roof worker was replacing flashing on a two-storey house. He used a tied ladder for access, but no roof ladder or edge protection. He fell from the roof; his body was found in the front garden by a passer-by.

Roof truss erection

87   A safe place of work should be provided when placing timber trusses on the wall plate and when fitting temporary and permanent bracing. Safe access will also be needed for fitting water tanks and services.

88   Prefabrication on the ground allows completed sections or whole roofs to be craned into place. This greatly reduces the need for work at height (see Figure 18).

Figure 18   *Craning a pre-assembled roof into position greatly reduces the need for work at height*

89   Where access is still needed, provide a safe working platform where practicable. This can be provided by boarding out immediately below the bottom chord of the truss. Any equipment used to gain access to higher levels of the truss should be properly designed and stable.

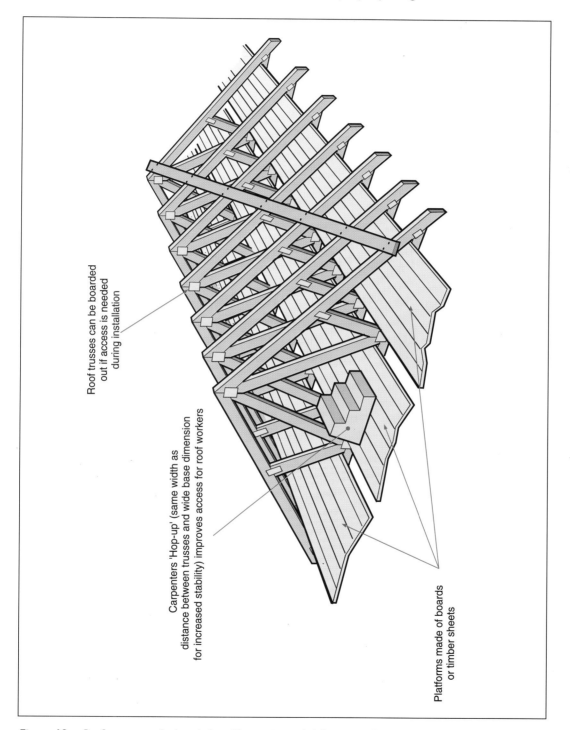

Roof trusses can be boarded out if access is needed during installation

Carpenters 'Hop-up' (same width as distance between trusses and wide base dimension for increased stability) improves access for roof workers

Platforms made of boards or timber sheets

Figure 19   *Roof trusses can be boarded out if access is needed during installation. Hop-up platforms improve access*

90   Working platforms can be supported by the truss members if they are stable and capable of sustaining the load. Guard rails should be provided unless truss members provide a similar standard of protection. Work below should be prohibited unless effective measures are taken to protect against falling materials (see Figure 19).

91   Fall arrest equipment such as nets or harnesses should only be relied on where a working platform to the standard described above are not feasible. Where it is used:

*   Attachment points must be fit for purpose, eg where blockwork is used to support nets, time must be allowed for the mortar to cure and attain sufficient strength to sustain the load should a fall occur.
*   The risk of injury during the fall, eg from striking parts of the rafters or blockwork, needs to be carefully assessed.
*   Working platforms should be provided as far as reasonably practicable in addition to the measures taken to arrest a fall.

See Appendices 2 and 3 for further information.

92   Rafters and rafter bundles should be stored so that they will be stable under foreseeable conditions.[11] If they are to be stored on a scaffold, scaffold designers should be made aware of this. They can then consider additional loading in the design. The scaffold platform can be extended to allow for safe storage and buttressing can be included to ensure stability of the trusses.

93   A crane or other mechanical handling device should always be used for lifting trusses unless this is not reasonably practicable. Good planning and design will reduce the need for manual handling. For instance, site layout designs can consider the need for crane locations. Work plans can then allow for cranage areas to be clear of other activities when trusses are installed. If manual handling has to be used, then a safe system of work should be devised (see Figures 20(a) and (b)). Manual handling should only be used where trusses are a suitable size and weight and structures are no more than two storeys high.

94   Work programming should include adequate time for the supporting structure to attain sufficient strength before roof construction begins. For example, blockwork should be adequately cured. Gable walls are usually unstable until tied into the roof assembly and can collapse during truss erection. Unless steps are taken to ensure stability, gable walls should be completed after the trussed rafter roof construction. Party wall construction in terraced units should follow the same principle unless temporary restraint is provided. Safe access for the bricklayers will need to be planned in for any work that cannot be done from the eaves scaffold.

95 Roof designers can contribute substantially to safe working. For example, they can design temporary and permanent bracing which can be fitted from a safe place. (See paragraphs 205-206.)

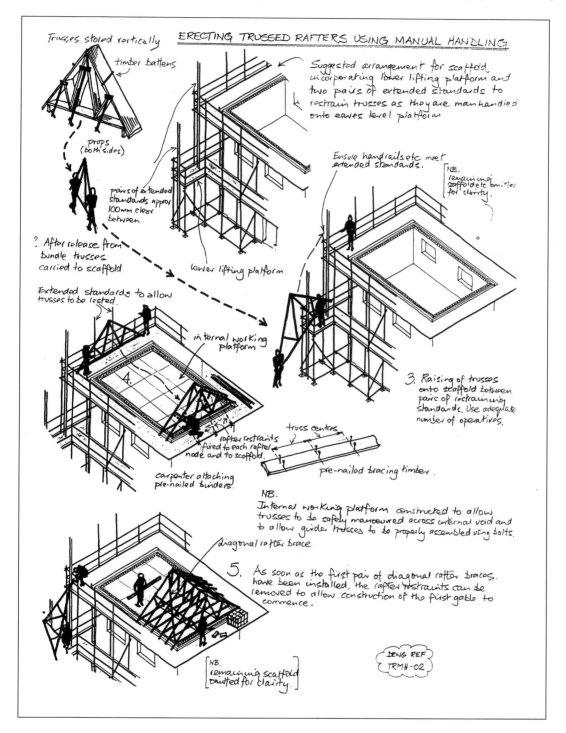

Figure 20(a) *Suggested system of work for roof truss erection. Note that simple diagrams can form the basis of 'user friendly' method statements*

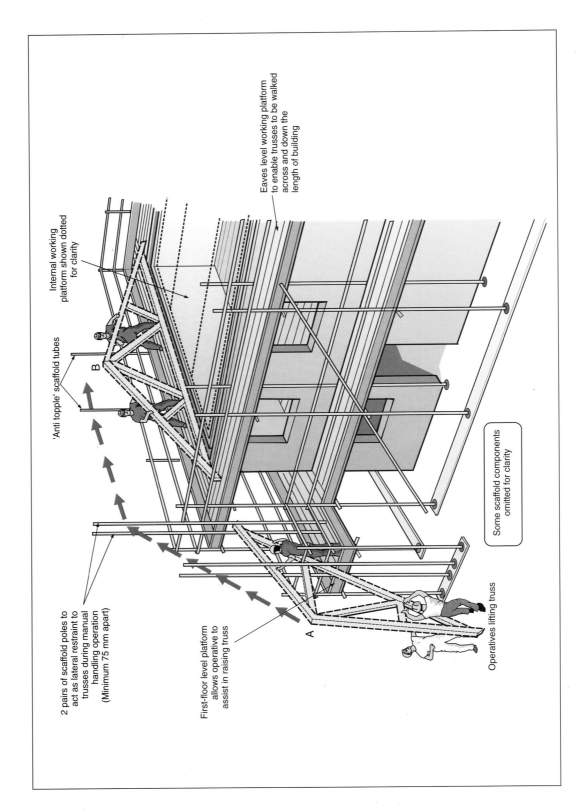

Eaves level working platform to enable trusses to be walked across and down the length of building

Internal working platform shown dotted for clarity

'Anti topple' scaffold tubes

B

Some scaffold components omitted for clarity

2 pairs of scaffold poles to act as lateral restraint to trusses during manual handling operation (Minimum 75 mm apart)

First-floor level platform allows operative to assist in raising truss

A

Operatives lifting truss

Figure 20(b)   *Suggested method for manual lifting of trusses to eaves level*

Fragile roofs

96   Falls through fragile material give rise to more fatal accidents in the construction industry than any other single cause. These deaths occur in both construction and maintenance, involving a whole range of fragile materials.

97   The terms 'fragility' and 'fragile material' are used in this document to describe a material or assembly which will not safely support the weight of a person and any materials they may foreseeably be carrying. This is discussed more fully in Appendix 4.

98   Assessment of fragility needs to take account of real life as well as theoretical conditions. For example, the tolerance on minimum distance between fixings and the edge of the sheet should take into account foreseeable errors in positioning, eg at any underlap. (Selecting materials which do not depend on the number or quality of fixings avoids these factors.) This is particularly relevant to liner panels and roof lights in built-up roofs.

99   Appendix 4 refers to tests which have been used to indicate fragility. Some typical examples of materials which have failed are:

- roof lights;
- liner panels on built-up roofs;
- fibre cement sheets;
- corroded metal sheets;
- glass (including wired glass); and
- wood wool slabs.

100   Falls through fragile materials are a particular problem in building maintenance. They cause over one quarter of deaths in this sector. Everyone with responsibility for this type of work, at whatever level, should treat it as a priority. This is particularly important for small, short-term maintenance and cleaning jobs. These might otherwise escape the assessment and planning given to higher value work (see paragraphs 47-50).

> *A roofing contractor was carrying out minor repairs to a farm barn. He was working on asbestos cement sheets, and was 'walking the purlins,' when he fell through the roof and sustained fatal head injuries. No equipment or safe system of work was provided.*

> *Two roof workers fell 5 m through an asbestos cement roof over a vehicle repair workshop. They were replacing the sheeting. No precautions were taken to prevent falls from or through the roof. Both were injured, one fatally.*

101   The long-term solution to this problem lies with designers and their clients, by eliminating all unprotected fragile roof materials in new and refurbished structures. However, the problem will remain in existing buildings for many years. The industry will also have to deal with temporary 'fragility' of partly fixed roofs, and deteriorated and damaged structures. Clients or occupiers should consider a permit-to-work system to control access to roofs with fragile coverings.

> **Fragile roof accidents are not inevitable. They can be prevented by careful planning, suitable equipment and a high level of supervision.**

102   If possible, work should be arranged so as to avoid working on or passing near fragile material. If this is unavoidable, it is essential to identify all fragile materials and decide on and implement stringent precautions. This applies to all operations on the roof, whether construction, maintenance, repair, cleaning or demolition (see Figure 21).

Figure 21   *Cleaning an asbestos cement roof using a self-contained water fed brush unit. There is no need for access onto the roof sheets and the guard rails prevent workers falling onto them (note: waste water is filtered before disposal)*

103   Some roof coverings can give a false sense of security to those who are working on or passing by them. They may be capable of carrying some distributed load, giving the impression that they can bear a person's weight. But they might **not** carry a concentrated load, eg the heel of a person walking, or a person stumbling and falling.

104   For example, asbestos and other fibre cement sheeting is liable to shatter without warning under a person's weight, even when newly installed. They will also become more brittle with age. A common but fatal belief persists that it is safe to walk along the line of the roof bolts above the purlins. This is walking a tightrope: one false step or loss of balance can lead to disaster. It should **not** be assumed that double skin roofs are safe: each layer can fail independently.

105   Plastic roof lights discolour with age. They may, in the past, have been painted to reduce glare, making them very difficult to identify. In some cases, insulation has been applied externally to a roof that is substantially load bearing, but contains fragile roof lights. This results in the roof lights being obscured. Roof surveyors should look for signs of repair, etc (see Figure 22).

Figure 22   *In some light conditions, it is difficult to distinguish the roof lights from the metal sheets on this type of roof. A labourer cleaning the gutter was seriously injured when he fell 9 m after stepping onto a roof light. The valley gutter is very narrow and roof lights extend down to gutter level, both of these features increase the risk during cleaning, maintenance or refurbishment.*

106   If any material is applied which may disguise fragile parts of a roof, the fragile parts should be clearly marked, and the information recorded. It should be included in any health and safety file for the building or any permit-to-work system for the roof. Warning notices should be erected at access points (see paragraphs 117-118).

107   Wood wool slabs may be liable to fracture beneath a person's weight. The following should be treated as fragile:

- wood wool slab less than 75 mm thick without a nylon net reinforcement;
- wood wool slab with a nylon net reinforcement but less than 50 mm thick;

- wood wool slabs which are wet or previously damaged;
- all straw board slabs, but especially those affected by water;
- all slabs where it is not possible to determine either their condition or the specific type which has been used.

> **Assume roof coverings to be fragile unless confirmed otherwise by a competent person.**

108   In some situations the structure supporting the roof covering may deteriorate so much that the roof can become 'fragile' and could fail catastrophically. In such a situation, eg where timber deterioration is a possibility, a thorough survey is essential.

Preventing falls through fragile material

109   A safe working platform on the roof, and safe access to the working position must be provided:

- platforms or coverings **must** be provided and used to support the weight of any person **on** fragile material;
- guard rails or coverings are required to prevent a person who is passing or working **near** fragile material from falling through.

110   Stagings (of a minimum 600 mm width) fitted with guard rails meeting the standard in paragraph 65 can be used where the roof pitch permits. There should be sufficient available to allow the work to be carried out safely. Operators should not have to continually move stagings to progress over the roof.

111   Where it is not practicable to maintain guard rails on both sides of the staging, other precautions will be required, for example:

- safety nets (see Figure 23);
- birdcage scaffolds.

These give maximum freedom to workers on the roof and can protect people working below, eg in a refurbishment project (see Appendix 2).

112   Harness and line systems can also form part of the system of work. They rely on operator training and a high level of supervision. The quality of the attachment system is critical. There are also minimum heights below which the system will be ineffective. In this case, a person may hit the floor before the restraint is fully operational. See Appendix 3 for further guidance.

Figure 23   *Safety netting used to provide protection for roof lights during minor roof works*

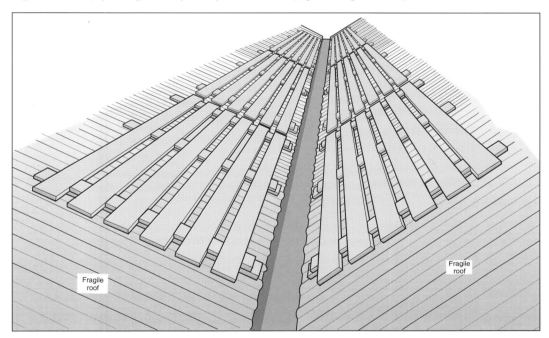

Figure 24   *Permanent protection installed at valley gutter (The protection should be supported by at least 3 rafters beneath the roof sheets)*

113   Precautions must also be taken to prevent falls from roof edges and working ('leading') edges (see paragraphs 130-140).

114   Where a valley or parapet gutter is used for access, precautions should be taken to prevent a person falling through fragile material in an adjacent roof. Where access along gutters is necessary on a regular (even if infrequent) basis, then permanent protection should be provided. Where practicable, this should provide collective rather than individual protection. Fixed covers, for example, are preferable to running line systems (see Figure 24).

115   Covers should extend far enough up the roof to provide protection to anyone falling against them. This is normally up to 2 m, depending on the roof pitch: shallower pitches will require more extensive coverage than steeper ones. Do not forget that protection such as safety nets or a birdcage scaffold is needed when covers are being installed. Valley gutters which are overhung by roof sheets so much that there is not enough space for a person's feet should not be used for access along the roof. It should be possible to clean the gutters without removing walkways or covers.

116   Roof lights should not extend within 2 m of valley gutters. Where fragile roof lights have already been fitted in this position and access is needed, permanent protection of the roof lights should be considered.

117   Precautions should be taken to prevent unauthorised access to fragile roofs. This will normally involve people at work, but the likelihood of unauthorised public access may need to be considered as well, particularly by children (see *Protecting the public - your next move* HSG151).[9] A risk assessment made under the Management of Health and Safety at Work Regulations 1992 is likely to require signs warning of the hazard and prohibiting access except under controlled conditions, eg governed by a permit-to-work regime. Permanently fixed ladders can be blocked off by boards whenever access is not required. Figure 25 illustrates a suitable sign which should be fixed at the approaches to roofs with fragile coverings. Such signs should be durable, securely fastened and properly maintained. Any signs used should meet the requirements of the Health and Safety (Safety Signs and Signals) Regulations 1996.[12]

Figure 25   *Typical fragile material warning sign*

118   Such signs are **not** an alternative to a designer's duty to get rid of hazards at source. Their function is to warn of dangers on existing buildings and where the load bearing properties of the roof coverings are unclear because of ageing, etc.

Industrial roofs

119   This section deals with industrial buildings (warehouses, factories, large retail, units, etc). These are typically steel framed, with roof cladding which can be:

- built up on site from liner panels, insulation and profiled metal top sheet;
- built up on site from structural decking, insulation and a weatherproof membrane; or
- factory assembled composite sheets which are laid as a single layer.

Roof pitches are usually low (8° or less) although steeper pitches are used for some applications.

Design issues

120   Designers need to consider a range of important issues. Paragraphs 191-200 discuss these in more detail.

Systems of work

121   Falls during industrial roofing commonly occur:

- through fragile roof lights;
- through gaps in the partially completed roof;
- through liner panels which are not fully fixed;
- from the leading (working) edge;
- from the edge of the roof or the gutter; and
- from the frame, eg when loading out roof sheets.

122   The system of work needs to include all stages of the job including delivery of materials (see Appendix 1). Simply loading out the frame with packs of sheets, as delivered, leads to workers travelling around the roof, past open edges, to get the correct length of sheet.

123   Ways of minimising travel on the roof include:

- use of hoists to deliver materials to the working position or to loading bays;
- providing access points convenient to the working positions;
- splitting packs of roof sheets to produce mixed packs in correct sequence for fixing; and
- back loading sheets onto the completed (load bearing) sections of roof.

See Figures 26 and 27

Figure 26   *Delivery of sheets to roof level onto the completed load bearing section and behind the leading edge. (Note that the roof lights include mesh protection and are non-fragile)*

124   Plan safe working positions and the means of access to and from those positions. Do not forget people who accept and unsling loads and who deliver sheets to the working position. For example:

* provide working platforms on the roof, fitted with guard rails and toe boards;
* use mobile access equipment;
* use safety nets;
* use safety harnesses together with suitable anchorage points.

It is **not** acceptable for the open steelwork or gutters to be used as the access or place of work without further precautions against a fall.

125   The weight of material should be limited to the amount that the structure can carry safely. Metal z-section purlins can twist and collapse under heavy loading. Sheets should be lashed to prevent their being dislodged or blown away. If necessary, stops should be used to prevent them slipping.

126   Falls from the edge of the frame can be prevented by edge protection. This is usually provided by an independent scaffold or barriers connected to the frame. An independent scaffold gives a higher standard of protection and also a good standard of access along the structure. It also assists material loading and storage, for example when used with a fork lift/telehandler.

Figure 27   *Scaffold loading bays can help to reduce material's movement on the roof. Suitable barriers should be provided to prevent falls at the open edge when loading is not taking place*

127   Falls through fragile materials, including liner panels, can be prevented by design (see paragraphs 191-198) along with carefully developed systems of work. In built-up roofs, the point at which all roof elements become load bearing at that span (the number and quality of fixings, use of reinforcing materials, etc) **needs to be absolutely clear for the combination of components used.** The implications of any changes in specification should be clearly identified.

128   Lining out the roof as quickly as possible in order to 'weather proof' the shell means the roof workers have to return in a second pass to lay the insulation and top sheets. Principal contractors should consider how this approach affects safe systems of work. If it is used, the specification of metal and roof light liners in terms of temporary fragility needs to be clarified. Adequate resources need to be allocated to achieve a safe system of work, eg by the use of safety nets.

129   Falls through gaps, eg for smoke vents, are a common cause of serious injuries and death. Designers can help by eliminating or reducing the number of openings. If there is a need for openings in the roof, the use of safety nets should be considered at the tender stage to protect both the gaps and the leading (working) edge.

> *A 24-year-old roof worker fell 29 m when he stepped onto a weakened area being prepared for the installation of a smoke vent. The upper sheet had been cut away. The lower sheet had been cut but not removed. It hinged and he fell through to the floor below.*

Leading edge protection

130   Controlling risk of falls at the leading (working) edge needs careful planning. Alternatives to be considered include:

*   safety nets;
*   birdcage scaffolds;
*   safety harnesses used with running line systems;
*   temporary barriers at the leading edge, eg trolley systems.

131   Because gaps are created during industrial roofing, fall arrest will almost always be required in addition to working platforms. Safety nets are the preferred solution for fall arrest. They give the roof workers maximum freedom of movement, provided that they do not work beyond their boundary. They can be installed in such a way as to minimise fall distances (see Appendix 2). They are effective where design details such as hips make other systems complex and difficult to manage. In a fall the chance of injury is reduced, compared to a similar one in a harness or onto a birdcage scaffold. Nets protect not just the leading edge, but also gaps, fragile areas, etc (see Figure 28).

132   Running lines designed to be used with a suitable harness/lanyard can be attached to the structure, to a mobile anchor point or to a working platform. Running line systems should be designed and tested to ensure that they are fit for purpose. The quality of the attachment point is critical, as is the type of harness (belts are not acceptable for fall arrest). See Appendix 3 for further information (see Figure 29).

Figure 28   *Industrial roof work: use of safety nets*

Figure 29   *Properly designed staging harness attachment system*

133   Harness users should be trained to fit and use them in accordance with the manufacturer's instructions. Excessive delay in rescuing a harness wearer who has fallen can result in permanent injury. The supplier's recommendations should be sought on the maximum time interval before someone is rescued following a fall. These emergency arrangements should then be included in the construction health and safety plan.

134   Where a running line is attached to the structure, the advice of the equipment supplier and the structural designer should be sought to make sure that the imposed loads can be sustained. Where it is attached to a working platform, the platform must be secured against overturning. Where a mobile anchor or inertial reel system is used, the number of workers approaching the leading edge should be minimised to reduce the risk of tripping and snagging.

135   Temporary barriers will be needed to control access to areas where harnesses have to be worn. Where running line systems are relied upon, access to the roof, eg during work breaks and at the end of the working day, needs to be controlled.

136   Temporary leading edge devices, eg purlin trolleys, are available and have been widely used. If locked in position, they can provide an effective guard rail at the leading edge when work is not in progress. The disadvantage is that installing and moving the systems can be high risk operations. When being used as a working platform, they often in practice provide little protection while laying and fixing sheets, as once the sheets are fixed, trolleys have to be moved, creating another gap in which to lay the next sheet.

137   In most situations, additional measures (usually in the form of fall arrest such as safety nets or harness and running line systems) are required to protect those using trolley systems from falling through the gap created to lay a new sheet or through fragile material such as partially fixed liner sheets. Manufacturers' recommendations on suitable anchorage points for running line systems should be followed. Horizontal guard rails on purlin trolleys or stagings are unlikely to be strong enough.

138   Trolley systems rely on the alignment of the supporting steelwork and the quality of the joints between purlins for the trolleys to run freely. Attempting to free trolleys which have jammed can be dangerous (see Figure 30). They are not suitable where design details such as hips, dormers, etc, do not allow adequate support over the full length of the trolley.

Figure 30   *Trolleys can sometimes become difficult to move which can force operators into dangerous positions*

139   Where trolleys are used:

- there should be a safe system for installing and/or assembling them on the roof specified in the method statement;
- the trolley attachment/locking system should be appropriate to the purlin design;
- a safe system for moving trolleys should be established;
- the joints between the purlins must allow the trolley to slide freely. Even minor misalignment can cause the trolley to jam and lead to unsafe systems of work;
- there should be a safe means of access to the trolley;
- when used as edge protection, the trolley must **always** be locked in position so that it can resist the turning moment of a person falling onto the guard rail;
- if there is risk of falling from the end of the trolley, eg at an unprotected ridge, a suitable barrier should be provided.

140   Figure 31 illustrates a system for laying composite sheets on a simple 'straight through' roof. This relies on properly planned movement of materials to avoid travel past the leading edge. Materials are delivered, as required, to a loading bay at the gable end. The work is co-ordinated so that open edges are minimised. Where work on adjoining slopes is out of phase (often the case at ridges and valleys) suitable barriers must be provided at open edges. It is vital that roof sheet length matches the trolley length.

Step 1

Step 2

Step 3

Figure 31   Laying composite sheets. Note: only one of these workers is protected against the sun.
They should all be

Protecting the public

141 The public may be at risk from falling materials during roof work. Precautions should always be taken to **prevent** materials falling where they may cause danger to anyone. This is particularly important where members of the public pass close to or below roof work.

142 Precautions are also needed to prevent people from being struck by any materials or tools which do fall and could cause injury. Birdcage scaffolds and debris netting can both be used to retain falling materials. Whatever system is chosen, it should be capable of retaining whatever is likely to fall. If material is stacked on a scaffold platform above the height of the toe board, proprietary brick guards will be needed to prevent material falling onto other workers or the public below. Where the public pass below or near to the scaffold then scaffold fans, tunnels or similar arrangements may be required.

> *A child walking down a pavement sustained head injuries when struck by a hammer dropped by a roof worker working on a residential property. A scaffold had been provided, but the edge protection was not adequate to contain falling materials.*

> *A member of the public suffered multiple injuries, including a fractured pelvis, femur and spine, when struck by falling edge protection from a roof. After the accident an independent tied scaffold was erected.*

A member of the public suffered serious head injuries when he was struck by a falling slate. A terraced house was being re-roofed. No edge protection was provided, and no precautions taken to prevent materials falling into the street.

143   Material may also fall through gaps in the working platform or between the working platform and the building. Sheeting, combined with a second layer of scaffold boards or plywood sheets, can be used to prevent this (see Figure 32). Care should also be taken not to overload the scaffold. If there is any risk of drips of hot bitumen falling from the roof edge, then physical protection or barriers at ground level may be necessary. See also Appendix 6.

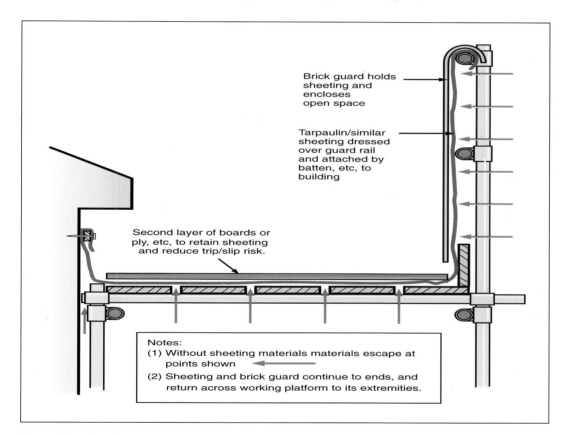

Brick guard holds
sheeting and
encloses
open space

Tarpaulin/similar
sheeting dressed
over guard rail
and attached by
batten, etc, to
building

Second layer of boards or
ply, etc, to retain sheeting
and reduce trip/slip risk.

Notes:
(1) Without sheeting materials materials escape at
    points shown
(2) Sheeting and brick guard continue to ends, and
    return across working platform to its extremities.

Figure 32   *Suitable protection where the public could be at risk from falling objects or materials*

144   Special precautions will be necessary where children may be put at risk, eg at or near schools or play areas, to keep them off scaffolding, etc. Where possible, roof work at schools should be done in holidays.

145   Waste materials such as old slates, tiles, etc, should never be thrown from the roof or scaffold. They should be lowered in skips or baskets designed for the purpose which will not spill material if snagged. Alternatively, enclosed debris chutes can be used. Chutes should be closed off to prevent their use when the skip below has been removed. Skips should be covered where necessary to protect the public from dust and flying materials.

146   Materials should not be hoisted over the public. Either:

- an alternative place for hoisting should be found, eg at the rear of the premises;
- alternative means of raising materials used; or
- a time chosen when the footpath, etc, can be closed (by agreement with the local highways authority).

Further detailed advice on protecting the public from the hazards of construction work is given in the HSE booklet *Protecting the public - your next move* HSG151.[9]

Controlling health risks

Manual handling

147 Lifting and moving loads by hand is one of the most common causes of injury at work. Handling heavy materials in awkward positions, eg rolls of roofing felt and long roof sheets, is a particular problem for roof workers. Many manual handling injuries result from repeated operations, but even one bad lift can cause a lifetime of pain and disability. The Manual Handling Regulations 1992 require employers to avoid manual handling which creates a risk of injury. Where it is not reasonably practicable to avoid this, employers have to make an assessment, reduce the risk of injury as far as is reasonably practicable, and give information about the weight of loads (see paragraphs 26-33).

Hazardous substances

148 Identify hazardous substances that are going to be used, or processes which may produce hazardous substances. The risks from work which might affect site workers or members of the public should then be assessed. Designers should try to avoid hazardous substances in their designs. Where this is **not** possible, they should specify the least hazardous products which perform satisfactorily.

149 Not all hazardous substances are generated by work activities. There may be waste or litter encountered when entering roof spaces. For example, substantial quantities of pigeon droppings in a confined space could give rise to a risk to health.

150   If workers use or are exposed to hazardous substances as a result of their work, the Control of Substances Hazardous to Health Regulations 1994 (COSHH) make it a legal duty to assess the health risks involved and to prevent exposure or else adequately control it.[13] There are separate regulations for asbestos and lead.[14, 15] HSE's booklet *Health risk management* HSG137 gives advice on how to identify and manage health risks.[16]

Asbestos

151   Asbestos-related disease kills more people than any other single work-related cause. Work with asbestos can release small fibres into the air. Breathing in these fibres can cause fatal diseases. But provided the asbestos is intact so that fibres are not released, it does not pose a risk to health .

152   Roof workers may be required to handle a number of materials containing asbestos, for example:

- cement sheets;
- roof tiles;
- insulation board, eg in soffits and roof linings;
- sprayed asbestos on structural roof members and applied as a coating to asbestos cement sheets;
- old asbestos pipe insulation in roof spaces.

153   Work with asbestos insulation or sprayed asbestos can only be undertaken by contractors licensed by HSE to carry out that type of work.

154   Work with asbestos insulation board requires specialist knowledge and equipment and is usually undertaken by licensed contractors.[14]

155   Work with asbestos cement sheeting does not require a license, but a number of simple precautions are necessary to prevent the spread of asbestos and control exposure.[17] Asbestos cement roof sheets are often removed during demolition work or prior to refurbishment. See Appendix 5 for guidance on the demolition of buildings with asbestos cement roofs.

Cleaning of asbestos cement roofs

156   Where possible this should be avoided. Before the decision is taken to clean this kind of roof, a thorough risk assessment should be carried out. Cleaning will release fibres. Work on the roof will inevitably involve substantial risk of falls. Any system of work adopted must control both these risks. High pressure water jets should not be used, as the contaminated slurry is difficult to contain.

Lead

157   Roof work can involve working with:

- lead flashing;
- lead sheeting and rain water goods;
- lead paint on structural steelwork.

158   Roof workers could be exposed to lead when:

- carrying out hot work/cutting/joining lead materials;
- removing or repairing old lead roofs.

159   The Control of Lead at Work Regulations 1998 require the assessment of any work which may expose people to lead. Guidance on control of exposure and good working practices is available.[15]

160   On construction sites, good welfare facilities should always be provided. They are the basis of controlling exposure to a number of common hazardous substances, including lead. Basic requirements are:

- a supply of hot and cold water and soap for washing;
- bowls/sinks big enough to allow hands and forearms to be washed easily before eating or drinking;
- clean towels.

161   Instruction and training are required to ensure that employees understand the risks, and the purpose of the control measures.

Bitumen and asphalt

162   Bitumen is derived from natural deposits or from petroleum refining. The term asphalt is usually used in the UK to mean a mixture of bitumen, stone and sand, etc. There is an occupational exposure standard for asphalt.[18]

163   COSHH 1994 requires employers to assess the exposure of roof workers to fume. Particular attention should be paid to:

- situations where natural ventilation is inhibited, eg by adjacent structures or architectural details;
- exposure of those who may be required to work in close proximity to bitumen boilers.

164   Suppliers of bitumen products will be able to advise on appropriate personal protective equipment to control inhalation of fume and to prevent contact with the skin.

Glues and solvents

165   Before specifying a product which may be hazardous to health, designers should consider whether a less harmful substance can be used instead. Relevant information should be included in the pre-tender health and safety plan.

166   Where designers have been unable to substitute less hazardous substances, then contractors will need to carry out an assessment of the risks and necessary precautions. Possible exposure routes include:

- breathing in the dust or fume;
- through the skin;
- by mouth, eg eating or smoking with contaminated hands.

167   Possible control measures include:

- brush application rather than spraying;
- ventilation to dilute or extract fume;
- a suitable mask which will absorb vapour before it is breathed in;
- gloves to prevent skin contact;
- adequate and accessible welfare facilities.

168   Instruction and training will be needed to ensure that risks and precautions are understood.

Ultraviolet radiation

169   Roof workers are exposed to sunlight. They are therefore at particular risk from the effects of ultraviolet radiation on the skin. Simple precautions can significantly reduce the risk of skin cancer. For example:

- suitable clothing;
- use of sun screens.

See the HSE publication *Keep your top on* INDG147 for further information. [19]

Training for roof workers

170 Roof work is potentially dangerous and roof workers need appropriate knowledge, skills and experience to do it safely. Otherwise they need to be under the supervision of someone who has those qualities.

171 Workers should be trained in safe working practices. It is not enough to hope that they will 'pick up' safety on the job from other workers - they might simply be learning someone else's bad habits. Employers need to be sure of their employees' abilities before setting them to work and provide necessary training where it is required. They will need training on the risks they will encounter (such as recognising fragile materials) and safe systems of work to control them. They may also need training in setting up and using equipment they are required to use. Typical examples would be:

- erecting a tower scaffold;
- setting up a hoist or lifting appliance;
- operating a mobile access platform; and
- rigging and inspection of safety nets.

172 Managers and supervisors need competence to deliver safety standards on site. To achieve this they will need health and safety training in order to:

- assess and prioritise the risks on a particular project;
- design safe systems of work that are appropriate to specific site conditions;

- prepare clear, simple safety method statements that can be used and understood by site workers.

173   First-line supervisors need to be able to interpret a safety method statement, in order to explain and follow a safe system of work.

174   Everyone who uses personal protective equipment should know how to use it effectively, for example:

- how to inspect the equipment to ensure that it will operate satisfactorily;
- how to fit and use a safety harness, following the manufacturer's recommendations;
- how to check the face fit of a respirator or dust mask.

175   Someone will need to be responsible for the firm's health and safety functions. This makes sure that health and safety is not missed or ignored. It also allows expertise to be built up in the firm. The person responsible may need extra training in health and safety to meet this responsibility properly.

The role of the client

176   Those who own, occupy or have responsibility for a building have an important role to play when arranging for roof work to be done. This includes considering the design and specification of a new building, appointing a contractor for refurbishment or instructing an employee to carry out an emergency roof repair.

177   Unrealistic building or refurbishment programmes can lead to undue pressure on those carrying out the work. This can make it harder for contractors to plan for safe working, to prepare quality safety method statements and to review and amend systems of work. Clients have an important role here. They should avoid placing unreasonable programming demands on the project.

178   For projects to which the CDM Regulations 1994 apply, clients must:

- Appoint a competent planning supervisor and principal contractor and check that any other designers or contractors they appoint are competent. Clients should satisfy themselves, as far as they reasonably can, that those they appoint to carry out work on the project are competent to do so and have the necesary resources. This could, for example, include inquiries on:
    - membership of relevant trade bodies or professional organisations;
    - previous experience of similar work;
    - arrangements for managing health and safety standards;
    - references from previous clients;
    - time needed to carry out the work safely.

- Provide relevant information needed to allow the work to be done safely. This could include information on:
    - what an existing roof is made of, especially if it contains fragile materials;
    - the age of an existing roof;
    - previous modifications made to an existing roof;
    - existing arrangements for access to the roof;
    - restrictions on availability of space for cranage;
    - any relevant permit-to-work arrangements operated by the client;
    - fire precautions on an occupied site;
    - areas where contractor access will be prohibited.
- Ensure that an adequate construction phase health and safety plan has been prepared by the principal contractor before work actually starts.
- If they dictate design details, eg that specific materials will be used, they should comply with the duties placed on designers by the CDM Regulations (see the next section *The role of the designer*).

179   The CDM Regulations will not apply to much smaller scale, short-lived roof work jobs. But even if CDM does not apply, its underlying principles of effective health and safety management can still be usefully followed. They will help clients to comply with their wide-ranging general duties under the Health and Safety at Work etc Act 1974 to exercise reasonably practicable care for the health and safety of themselves, their employees and others such as contractors and members of the public.

180   Duties on clients do not apply to private householders when they have construction work carried out on domestic property.

181   Clients can benefit considerably from a structured approach to health and safety. Better planning and better systems of co-ordination between designers, contractors and specialist subcontractors can lead to:

- reduced delays;
- a building that is easier and cheaper to maintain.

182   Work at height is more expensive than similar work done at ground level. This additional cost can increase dramatically if it is not properly organised and controlled.

The role of the designer

183 Using their professional skills and judgement, designers can eliminate hazards and make risks easier to manage. This helps contractors to provide a safer place of work on the roof. Designers need to consider the initial construction work as well as future maintenance and cleaning requirements.

184 Under the CDM Regulations designers have a duty to ensure that their designs give adequate regard to health and safety. Foreseeable risks should be avoided. If it is not reasonably practicable to avoid them, they should be combated at source. Priority should be given to design solutions providing general rather than individual protection. For example:

- eliminate unprotected fragile materials;
- minimise the need for work at height during construction;
- minimise inspection and maintenance requirements for the completed roof structure;
- identify and design in safe access and safe place of work for maintenance and cleaning (see Figure 33).
- consider carefully the siting of plant which will require maintenance. Are there alternatives to placing it on the roof? If not, is it in the optimum position on the roof where safe access can most easily be provided?
- consider carefully the siting of roof lights, (see Figure 34).
- provide clear and unambiguous specifications for safety critical elements of the design;
- provide information relevant to construction and maintenance for inclusion in tender documentation and in the health and safety file.

Figure 33

Permanent walkway giving safe access on a fragile roof. (This walkway was retro-fitted, but similar access can be included in initial designs)

Figure 34   *Lighting panels installed in the wall rather than the roof*

Example of risk elimination through design

On a major refurbishment of a large hangar, the fragile asbestos cement roof was replaced by load bearing metal sheets. After consultation with the client, the roof lights were replaced by translucent vertical panels below eaves level. This reduced risk of falls during the re-roofing and any subsequent maintenance (see Figure 34).

Examples of reduction/control of risk through design

The designer of a new shopping centre with a glass atrium recognised the risk of falling during cleaning and maintenance of glazed areas. An access system using mobile gantries was designed and installed and an inspection regime established for the equipment.

The designer of a 'built-up' industrial roof ensured that all components, eg liner panels, top sheets, insulation and fixings, were the same modular width. This reduced the risk to roof workers. They were able to adopt a system of work which restricted the area of temporarily fixed liner panels to a single sheet width.

185   Such outcomes will be easier to achieve if there is good liaison between:

- designer and client, eg on access requirements for maintenance;
- lead designer, specifiers and installers.

186   The design of the roof should be reviewed as a total design 'package'. It should take account of the interaction between all components (in both final and partially erected state) and their effect on the systems of work necessary to erect the structure.

187   The following paragraphs provide more detailed design guidance for particular roofing applications.

Designing flat and low pitch roofs

188   Access to these roofs is often simple and because they are flat it is easy to walk around on them. Accidents happen not just to roof workers but also to engineers, surveyors, children, caretakers, etc. The first priority is to design out the risk at source, for example by specifying adequate inbuilt edge protection. Designers should consider the alternatives available in terms of their effectiveness in preventing falls, as well as cost, aesthetics and buildability.

Edge protection

189 Edge protection options in order of effectiveness are:

- designed parapet (see Figure 35);
- guard rail at the roof edge (see Figure 36);
- permanent protected walkway for access to plant on the roof;
- preformed sockets to support temporary edge protection guard rails;
- running line systems designed, installed and tested to the relevant standards (see Appendix 3).

Figure 35   *Parapet edge protection included as an integral design feature*

Figure 36   *Permanent guard rail retro-fitted during refurbishment work. Similar protection can be included in initial designs*

190   Designers should be aware of the requirements of the Workplace (Health Safety and Welfare) Regulations 1992.[25]

Designing industrial roofs

191   The most important issue for designers is how to eliminate unprotected fragile material at height. **Designers should consider carefully the potential to eliminate or reduce this hazard.**

192   Whatever roof light and roofing sheet systems are used, the assembly should be tested to determine fragility and the relevant information passed on to those who may need it (see Appendix 4).

193   The health and safety file should include relevant information from the supplier, such as:

- tests results on the initial material strength;
- the effects of ultraviolet radiation on material properties;
- fixing specifications, including type, number and position.

Roof lights

194   **For roof lights designers should consider carefully the potential to eliminate or reduce this hazard.** The decision on whether to include roof lights should take account of the risks associated with temporary gaps during construction, and the risks when access to the roof is needed later, eg during maintenance or cleaning.

195   Where roof lights **are** required designers should consider:

- specifying roof lights that are non-fragile;
- fitting roof lights designed to project above the plane of the roof and which cannot be walked on (these reduce the risk but they should still be capable of withstanding a person falling onto them) (see Figure 37);
- protecting roof lights, eg by means of mesh or grids fitted below the roof light or between the layers of a built-up roof light (see Figure 38);
- specifying roof lights with a design life that matches that of the roof, taking account of the likely deterioration due to ultraviolet exposure, environmental pollution and internal and external building environment.

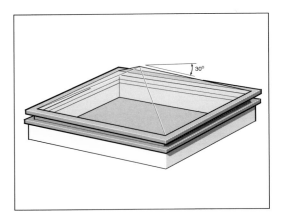

Figure 37   Typical 'out of plane'
                 polycarbonate roof light

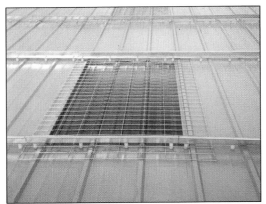

Figure 38   Galvanised mesh reinforcement between
                 sheets of twin skin roof light

Roofing sheets

196   The safest option for roof sheets is to specify a material which will be non-fragile for the design life of the roof. The norm should be to specify non-fragile roof sheets unless there are very particular design requirements which dictate other materials. These design criteria should be clearly documented.

197   The specification of **reinforced** fibre cement sheets can be considered These should still be considered fragile and appropriate precautions are needed when people work on or near them. However, they offer a less fragile alternative to non-reinforced sheets.

198   There are usually times during the laying of a built-up roof when coverings are non load-bearing, for example when not fully fixed. Designers need to consider this carefully and aim to eliminate or minimise this condition. The specification of liner sheets (thickness and profile) and, equally important, the fixing method should be assessed with these criteria in mind. The designer should supply precise information on the fixing configuration(s) which are load-bearing for a particular span and cladding material combination (see Appendix 4) so that contractors can develop a safe system of work.

> *A roof worker was working over a temporarily fixed roof liner panel, putting in permanent fixings. He fell 10 m to his death when the end of the sheet buckled under his weight.*

199   Composite roof sheets are quicker to fix and are often immediately load bearing independent of fixings. However, safe systems of work for handling these heavier sheets will need to be developed.

200   Handling very long roofing sheets can be dangerous for roof workers and others, even in moderate winds. Designers need to decide the maximum wind speed in which these sheets can be laid. They then need to find out about likely local weather conditions and this should indicate whether the proposed sheet lengths are appropriate or not. More detailed information is contained in guidance from the National Federation of Roofing Contractors.[5]

Roof maintenance

201   Designers can help reduce the amount of work done at height throughout the life of the structure. For example, they could:

- increase the maintenance life of roof elements;
- locate plant and equipment at low level wherever possible; and
- design gutter detailing to reduce blockages.

Co-operation with others

202   Good liaison between designers can achieve better standards at all stages of the work. A practical example is the effect of gutter design on systems of work when the roof is laid.

203   Roof workers and others commonly use gutters for access at eaves level along the roof. The structural strength of the gutter, its width and depth and the quality of the fixings greatly affect its safety as a means of access. Where gutters are not strong enough or are fitted after the roof cladding is fixed, means of access will be needed which take this into account. Problems can often be avoided if designers consult with each other.

204   There are a number of issues where the design of the frame of the structure has a direct effect on the systems of work of the roof workers. For example:

- if running lines are to be used during erection, then anchorage points need to be designed into the frame at appropriate points;
- the design and sizing of purlins and the alignment of the joints between purlins can determine whether or not a trolley system can be used successfully;
- the position of sag rods can affect systems of work;
- the design of eaves beams is relevant to the installation of nets and to the stability of scaffold tube edge protection.

Resolving these issues requires close co-ordination between frame and cladding designers.

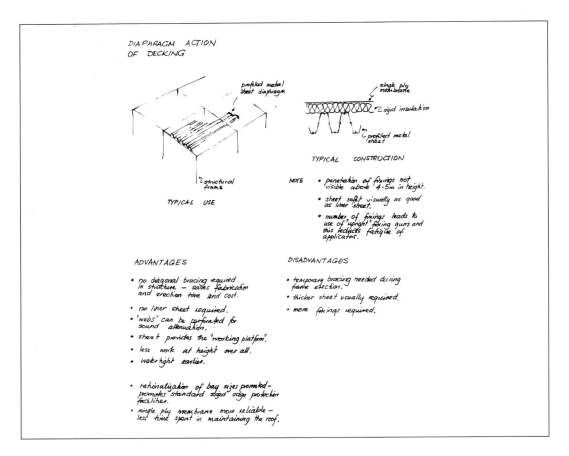

Figure 39   *Shows a generic risk assessment carried out by a designer for one **particular** design of industrial building. It illustrates the types of issues designers need to address*

Designing trussed roofs

205   Designers of trussed roofs can contribute to safe working by:

- designing both permanent and temporary bracing so that it can be fixed from a safe place;
- designing slinging points and, as appropriate, lifting attachments which allow truss bundles to be unslung from a safe place, eg the eaves scaffold;
- designing permanent bracing to allow trusses to be assembled into complete roof structures or modules on the ground and lifted into position;
- specifying slinging points for such assemblies;
- giving information on the bracing required before a working platform can be supported by the trusses.

206   As with other types of roofs, this approach requires co-operation between all designers involved, and also between designers and installers.

Planning for safety

207   Roof work includes all scales of project. It can include the initial construction of a roof, major refurbishment of an existing one, or minor work such as replacing a few tiles or chimney repairs on a house. Planning by client, planning supervisor (where CDM applies) and contractors helps to ensure work is carried out safely, efficiently and without undue delay.

208   Short duration work can be very high risk, eg minor repairs to a factory roof containing fragile roof lights. Accidents happen when such work is poorly planned, the proper equipment is not provided and roof workers are inadequately trained.

> *A machine operator died when he fell more than 9 m through a plastic roof light in a profiled steel industrial roof. He was intending to repair a roof light which was leaking onto a conveyor, but fell when crossing the roof.*

209   Roof work should only be undertaken by those with the knowledge, experience, training and resources to complete the work safely. Thorough planning, instruction and effective 'on the spot' supervision are essential for accident prevention.

210   A safety method statement should normally be prepared before work starts on a roof. It needs to be appropriate to the scale and complexity of the work. In all cases, it should ensure that risks are recognised and assessed and the appropriate control measures specified.

211   Safety method statements should be clear and illustrated by simple sketches. There should be no ambiguities or generalisations which could lead to confusion. They should be written for the benefit of those carrying out the work and their immediate supervisors. Equipment needed for safe working should be clearly identified. It should also be clear what to do if the work method needs to be changed. This should avoid 'ad hoc' methods of work on site and the use of improvised equipment (see Appendix 1).

212   The following sections describe what planning supervisors, principal contractors and contractors need to do when CDM applies. CDM will not apply to much short-term roof work. However, CDM is based on fundamental principles of effective health and safety management. Short-term roof work is high risk. Those managing or controlling it need to exercise effective management and procedures similar to CDM can still be used for this purpose.

Planning supervisors

213   Planning supervisors will have an important role to play where CDM applies.
For example:

- if requested by the client, they will advise on competence of designers and contractors;
- they will ensure that a pre-tender health and safety plan for the project is prepared;
- they may advise the client on the adequacy of the health and safety plan for the construction phase.

214   The pre-tender health and safety plan should answer these basic questions:

- What are the major health and safety risks on this project?
- Are significant resources needed to control these risks?
- What specific competencies are required to carry out the work safely?

215   The pre-tender health and safety plan should then:

- set out any basic assumptions about how the work will be done to control the significant risks, eg use of safety nets for industrial roofs, use of mobile access equipment to install gutters and erect edge protection;
- identify programming implications of safe systems of work, eg provision of suitable ground conditions for mobile access equipment, allowing time for blockwork to cure before trusses are installed;
- identify any aspects of the client's activities having health and safety implications, eg times when significant vehicle movements can be expected;
- clarify any other specific requirements by the client, eg for repairs to a school roof, the client might specify that work is done during school holidays.

For a new warehouse, the pre-tender health and safety plan identified work at height as the major risk on the project. A method statement was not required at this stage, but contractors were asked to state clearly how falls were to be prevented during roof cladding and gutter fixing. The principal contractor's tender proposal indicated:

- the use of scissor lifts for gutter fixing;
- the use of safety nets for the roof cladding operation.

216 The pre-tender health and safety plan should contain relevant information provided by the client or by designers, for example:

- the load bearing capacity of a flat roof;
- ground conditions and access for crane(s);
- information from the designer on sequence of erection, temporary stability and bracing of trussed roofs;
- presence of asbestos insulation board in soffits;
- presence of sprayed asbestos on trusses or purlins;
- position and type of overhead power lines including those associated with railways;
- design information on fixing details necessary to ensure non-fragility.

Principal contractors

217 Principal contractors are the key players in setting practical on-site safety standards and making sure that they are actually followed. They should:

- ensure that the overall work programme gives enough time for work to be done safely by the roofing sub-contractor, taking account of likely weather conditions;
- allow time to consider method statements and deal with the implications of design changes;
- devise a work programme which reflects the need to control access to areas below roof work where there is danger of falling materials;
- specify clearly at tender stage the resources allocated to control and manage risks such as falls from height;
- ensure that relevant information is passed to the roofing contractor.

218 Principal contractors need to ensure that an adequate construction phase health and safety plan is in place **before** construction starts. The plan needs to set out explicitly how the work is to be done in practice and the precautionary measures that need to be taken.

219   Safety-method statements can usefully form the basis of the construction phase health and safety plan. They are usually drawn up by individual contractors rather than the principal contractor. Principal contractors need to scrutinise contractor method statements. They need to satisfy themselves that these are appropriate and adequate for the work in hand. It is not acceptable for principal contractors to merely specify that method statements are drawn up. They need to establish an effective system for reviewing them. (See Appendix 1.)

220   Principal contractors need to monitor compliance with the construction phase health and safety plan and take positive action to remedy matters if risk is not being effectively controlled.

Contractors

221   Contractors need to:

* prepare safety-method statements that are relevant to the work being done;
* ensure that they and their employees are competent to carry out the work in hand safely;
* co-operate with the principal contractor in implementing the construction phase health and safety plan.

Appendices

APPENDIX 1   Issues for method statements in industrial roof work

> *This appendix is **not** a method statement. It indicates the issues that method statements need to consider for industrial roof work. A similar analytical approach is appropriate for other roof work.*

1   This is **high-risk work** which requires the closest attention to detail at all stages of the work. There should be a job-specific **method statement** in writing, agreed and understood by all parties **before work starts. Rigorous supervision is needed to ensure that the agreed method is followed in practice. There should also be a system to allow necessary changes to be made and confirmed.**

Method statements should be clear, concise and include simple sketches.

2   The following general questions are particularly relevant to a low pitch industrial roof consisting of liner sheet, insulation layer and profiled metal top sheet. This is not an exhaustive checklist, but is intended to act as a prompt when method statements are prepared and reviewed.

3   Non-standard or unusual systems will require special consideration. There may also be risks specific to an individual site which will need to be addressed (eg the presence of overhead power lines).

Risk of falling, eg getting on/off ladders at eaves

Access to roof: have access points been discussed with the roofing gang in order to reduce travel over the roof to a minimum? If ladders are used (as opposed to towers) are means available for hoisting smaller components not craned up? Has the stability of long ladders been considered, eg will they need staying to reduce whip?

Risk of falling when walking past open edges to fetch materials

Materials handling: how are roofing packs loaded out onto the roof? Is this planned so as to reduce travel when fetching sheets and does it allow for protected routes/safe means of access? Splitting packs of different sheet size and reassembling them at ground level can save travel at height. Back loading sheets onto the completed roof can reduce travel past open edges.

Risk of falling from steel frame when unslinging

Cranes: if one is used, who will accept the load or unsling it? How will they be protected from falling? Has the use of mobile access equipment been considered for this task?

Risk of falling outside building frame exists at all stages of work. Gable ends are particularly hazardous

Edge protection: does the programme ensure that eaves, gable ends and other open edges are protected before work starts? Protection will also be required at ridges unless work progresses at the same rate on both roof slopes. What are the access arrangements for those installing edge protection?

Risk of falling on both sides of gutter ie inside and outside building frame

Gutter fixing: how will workers be protected from falling? Peripheral edge protection erected for roof workers will not be sufficient at this phase. Has the use of mobile access equipment been considered as a first priority? If the use of a running line or harness and lanyard is specified, who will erect and test the line?

Risk of falling from partly completed roof

Leading edge protection: how will this be achieved? Has the use of safety nets been considered in the light of legal duties and risk assessment for the total roofing operation? Stagings used as working platforms should be stable and of adequate width with handrails/running lines specified to suit the working practices. Work done kneeling/bending needs careful attention as the operator's centre of gravity can extend over the leading edge. What method is specified for moving stagings?

Is the method of work to be adopted when laying the first sheet specified? Some architectural features, eg hip ends, will require modifications to the working methods. These should be fully described.

Has fixing of ridge capping/flashing been included in the system of work? Is effective edge protection provided at the gable end of the ridge?

Does the method statement make it clear at what stage of construction materials such as liner panels become load-bearing? The number and type of fixings required should be stated. Until this is achieved, they **must** be treated as fragile materials, ie unable to sustain a person's weight, and protection provided as above.

Have any **fragile** materials been specified by the designer? If so, this design decision should be reviewed by the designer as a matter of urgency in terms of duties under the CDM Regulations.

For refurbishment work on existing roofs, are there any fragile materials on the roof, eg roof lights? These will have to be protected. How will this be achieved? If covers are to be used, are they strong enough, taking account of the span required? How will they be fixed and what is the system for their removal?

Zoning of the roof into working and non-working areas can reduce the number of roof lights which need to be protected. The system for marking out the zones and for progressing the work should be specified. If barriers marking the edge of the zones are within 2 m of fragile material, then they must be strong and rigid enough to support the weight of a person who loses their balance.

Zoning should take account of travel to the working area by the roof workers and also the need for materials to be moved around the roof. The system should ensure that all roof lights within working zones and adjacent to access routes are protected.

Systems control   **Communications**: what are the arrangements for ensuring that the method statement is communicated **to** and agreed **with** the roofing gang?

Supervision: what are the arrangements for ensuring that the work proceeds according to the method statement?

Modifications: what are the arrangements for agreeing any modifications to the method statement and ensuring that these are communicated to the roofing gang?

Validation: what are the arrangements for ensuring that the company safety adviser or other nominated competent person has reviewed, and is satisfied with, the system of work proposed?

APPENDIX 2 Use of safety nets

1   Safety nets can be effectively employed to reduce potential falls and to minimise their effects. They offer collective, passive safety as they protect everyone working within their boundary, without requiring those workers to act to be protected. They allow a broad range of activity to continue with minimum restriction.

2   Safety nets have high energy absorbtion capability, and therefore offer a 'soft landing' that minimises injury. They should always be fitted **as close as possible to the underside of the working platform.**

3   Lightweight, square mesh nets offer the flattest span (less than 10% sag). In most roof work it is possible to position such a net so that, even at the point of maximum sag, it is less than 2 m from the roof surface. In this position the net is an effective guard and this standard should be attained wherever possible.

4   Safety nets overlaid with an appropriate fine mesh debris cover can also protect those who have to work or pass below. Consideration should be given to the type of materials likely to fall, eg fixings or tools, when selecting the overlay material. Safety nets have the additional advantage that materials are contained by the net and do not bounce.

5   Safety nets can be effectively employed:

* to prevent injury due to falls from leading edges through liner panels, or temporarily fixed materials in new build roofing;
* to guard roof lights and fragile roof materials during cleaning, maintenance and replacement of the roof; and
* to prevent injury from falls during roof truss erection, eg when fitting diagonal bracing.

Relevant standards

6   Safety nets should be manufactured to the requirements of the European Standard EN 1263: Part 1[20] and should be erected in accordance with EN 1263: Part 2.[21] The standard describes four basic types of safety nets. The nets described in this guidance are Type S. This is the standard horizontal safety net with border cord that is designed to be sized and fixed to the building structure. EN 1263: Part 2 covers the main technical information for the use of these nets. British Standard 8093 gives much information on the installation and use of safety nets.[22]

Design and technical details

7   When rigging safety nets it is important to maintain their energy absorbing characteristics. Too many fixing points and the net becomes more rigid and imposes larger loads on the user, the structure and the net itself. Too few fixing points and the net will sag too greatly and deflect too much under load. The manufacturer's recommendations and the British Standard Code of Practice should be followed on the number and spacing of fixing points. Checks need to be made to ensure that the supporting structure is capable of resisting the expected anchorage loads.

8   Wherever possible nets should be rigged so as to prevent falls of 2 m or more. If they are to be used for the arrest of falls greater than 2 m, they should have:

*   an area greater than 35 m^2;
*   a minimum side length (width) greater than 5 m;
*   maximum support spacing 2.5 m;
*   an individual anchor point capacity of 6 kN, applied at 45° to the horizontal;
*   a combined capacity over an adjacent series of anchor points of 4 kN, 6 kN, 4 kN.

9   Adequate clearance must be allowed below the net to allow it to function properly. The manufacturer's recommendations should be followed for the minimum clearance which should be free of all obstructions.[20]

10   Safety nets must extend beyond the leading edge of the work by at least the minimum catching width. This is linked to fall height (see Table 1).

Table 1 Fall heights and catching widths

Fall height	< 1.0 m	< 3.0 m	< 6.0 m
Catching width	> 2.0 m	> 2.5 m	> 3.0 m

11   The maximum general fall height is 6 m. However, this is reduced to 3 m within 2 m of the supported edge of the safety net, to take account of the reduced capacity for energy absorbtion near the fixed edge.

Planning

12   When planning the use of safety nets, the technical aspects should be taken into consideration. It is feasible to pre-position safety net attachment points (eg welded lugs) onto primary steel work, for use when erecting the building. These would then be available to support safety nets when building maintenance is needed and also for eventual demolition.

Erection

13   Safety nets can be connected by designed attachment points or by flexible tie ropes to primary steelwork of suitable capacity, or to other selected anchorage points. Nets can be moved and removed as the work progress demands.

14   The risk to riggers erecting, moving and dismantling nets should be assessed and a safe system of work established. Access equipment such as mobile towers or mobile elevating work platforms (MEWPs) should be capable of resisting any imposed sideways loading during net installation. In existing buildings there may be permanently installed access equipment. This may be used if suitable for the imposed loads. Roped access techniques may be appropriate in some buildings. This is specialised work and should only be undertaken by those trained and competent to carry it out.[23]

15   Those who erect nets should be aware of the relevant standards, trained and be competent to carry out the work safely. This may require the use of specialist installers and riggers, especially where large nets are being used.

APPENDIX 3   Use of safety harnesses and running line systems

1   A fall arrest system should be the last choice for protection against falls from height. There is still a possibility of injury in an arrested fall. The system relies on the user accepting the discipline to ensure that the equipment is consistently and effectively used. There will be circumstances, however, when it is not reasonably practicable to provide physical measures to prevent a person falling. In such cases, a full body harness attached to a suitably anchored system incorporating some form of energy absorber may be the only precaution available. This at least ensures that if a fall occurs, it is safely arrested.

2   Fall arrest systems come in a variety of forms. These range from a single lanyard or a retractable type fall arrester attached to a fixed anchorage point through to a number of lanyards with mobile attachment points on a single horizontal flexible anchorage line or a proprietary multi-span cable-based system. All should be used with full body harnesses. The system should incorporate some form of energy absorber or energy dissipating element to ensure that the deceleration forces on the user do not exceed 6 g. Fall arrest systems serve as personal protective equipment (PPE) against falls from height.

3   The provision and use of fall arrest equipment is subject to the Personal Protective Equipment at Work Regulations 1992. There are a number of relevant European Standards specifying the requirements for fall arrest systems and components, namely:

*   *PPE against falls from height. Part 1 Specification for guided type fall arrestors on a rigid anchorage line* BS EN 353: Part 1 1993
        PPE against falls from height. Part 2 Specification for guided type fall arrestors on a flexible type anchorage line BS EN 352: Part 2 1993
*   *PPE against falls from height. Lanyards* BS EN 354: 1993
*   *PPE against falls from height. Energy absorbers* BS EN 355: 1993
*   *PPE against falls from height. Retractable type fall arrestors* BS EN 360: 1993
*   *PPE against falls from height. Full body harnesses* BS EN 361: 1993
*   *PPE against falls from height. Connectors* BS EN 362: 1993
*   *PPE against falls from height. Fall arrest systems* BS EN 363: 1993
*   *PPE against falls from height. Test methods* BS EN 364: 1993
*   *PPE against falls from height. General requirements for instructions for use and for marking* BS EN 365: 1993

4   The safe performance of a fall arrest system depends completely on a suitable anchorage being provided. This could be a single fixed anchorage point or a flexible anchorage line. The adequacy of all anchorages, including the ability of the supporting structure to carry the anchorage loads, should be verified by calculation or by testing. For example, the structural

adequacy of a guard rail to resist fall arrest forces should be assessed before a lanyard and harness are anchored to it. Anchorages should generally be installed as high as possible, preferably above the user and never below foot level. Retractable type fall arresters should only be anchored at chest height or above.

5   In order for a fall arrest system to function correctly there must be adequate clearance below. For example, a system comprising a full body harness and a 2 m long lanyard with an energy absorber anchored at foot level could require up to 6.25 m of clearance below the anchorage. This is made up as follows:

- 2 m, original length of the lanyard plus shock absorber;
- 1.75 m, maximum allowable extension of the shock absorber;
- 2.5 m, allowance to cover the displacement of the full body harness and the clearance below the feet of the user after the arrest.

When a flexible anchorage line system is used, allowance must also be made for the sag of the line between anchorages.

6   Consideration should also be given to how a person would be rescued after an arrested fall, particularly from high structures.

7   Adequate information, instruction, training and supervision should be given when a fall arrest system is used. For example:

- how to wear the harness and adjust it to the body;
- how to manage the lanyard and other equipment;
- how to fall so as to minimise the risk of injury;
- how to self rescue or assist others after a fall;
- how to inspect the equipment and recognise significant defects;
- how to assemble the system correctly, including recognition of the importance of safe anchorages.

8   Fall arrest systems are not foolproof and their safe usage is not always common sense. Without proper training in fitting, use, maintenance, installation and equipment limitations, all that a fall arrest system can provide is a false sense of security.

APPENDIX 4   Fragility: tests and specifications

1   This appendix does not constitute a technical definition or specification of fragility. It provides information to help readers decide whether a particular material used in particular circumstances can be considered fragile or not. It is essential to understand that fragility depends on a range of issues. It **is not** solely determined by the nature of the material. All these issues need to be considered when assessing fragility.

2   What is fragile or non-fragile in the terms of this guidance, depends on whether or not an element may fail under under a person's weight or whether it will support a person by a comfortable safety margin. The structural capability of the element is related to the loads carried, and whether these are static or dynamic.

3   In this appendix an 'element' means a roof light, an area of sheeting or similar. This includes all the fixings and supports for the element as well as the materials used in its construction. For a site-assembled double skin system, the liner sheets for both metal and plastic roof lights should be considered as elements in their own right and tested as such. Safe systems of work for the initial construction of such a roof depend on information on the fragility of liners related to laps and fixings.

4   If a person fell through an element it would clearly have failed and so be considered fragile. It would also fail if it temporarily supported the person after the initial impact only to collapse a short time afterwards so that the person fell. For this reason elements should have a suitable reserve of strength after initial impact. This can be seen as a 'margin of safety' to allow the person to escape from the broken element before total failure could occur.

5   The capability of an element to withstand loads depends on the nature of the material used and its configuration, eg:

- thickness;
- span;
- profile;
- the type of fixings used;
- the quality of fixings, eg material specification;
- the number and position of fixings; and
- the design of the supporting structure, eg purlin specification including thickness and flexibility.

6   It may also depend on the age of the material, for example, the effects of weathering, ultraviolet degradation, corrosion, mechanical damage and chemical attack on the materials can all have a profound effect on fragility.

7   In interpreting test results and material specifications it is important to consider the mode of failure, eg:

- Elements such as PVC sheet roof lights have so little inherent strength that they fail catastrophically. There is little problem in interpreting test data to conclude fragility.
- Membrane materials (eg lightweight GRP roof lights) typically fail at the fixing points. For these materials it is essential that testing includes examination of the fixing arrangements as well as the material itself. Testing should take account of the 'worst case scenario' which for this type of material could be a load imposed at a corner of the sheet.
- Materials such as fibre cement sheets fail suddenly in bending. Fixings are less critical and the worst case is an imposed load in the centre of the sheet.
- Span is critical and these materials should not be used for larger spans than those tested.

8   The loading imposed will vary depending on the weight of the person and any loads being carried. It also depends on whether the person steps onto the element, falls on it, falls against it or strikes it with part of or the whole body. These variations all have a significant effect on the area and velocity of impact.

Testing for fragility

9   HSE's Specialist Inspector Report No. SIR 30 shed more light on the technical meaning of fragility. However it cannot be considered a universally definitive interpretation of fragility. It does not take into account the full range of variable factors described above. It describes a test where a 45 kg sandbag is dropped onto the centre of an element. If the test weight passes through the element then this indicates fragility. Similar tests are described in the standards of various European countries, but they should not be regarded as comprehensively definitive, any more than the test described in SIR 30.

10   There are three main reasons for the limited usefulness of such tests:

- the test mass does not properly represent the effect of a person jumping, falling or stepping onto the element;
- no indication of the safety margin at failure is given; and
- while they may give some indication about the material they are a poor test of how the material is fixed.

11   At present detailed information is not available on how the relationships between these criteria can be resolved in testing. Research work is currently being undertaken to clarify them.

12   Until the research results are available the following 'rules of thumb' may be used to help decide on the fragility of different materials, of a thickness commonly used in roofing applications.

- PVC: This should always be considered fragile.

- Acrylic: This is particularly vulnerable to ultraviolet degradation. It should therefore be considered as fragile for all but very short-term uses.

- Polycarbonate: This is available with coatings that protect against the effects of ultraviolet light and is itself a structurally strong material. It can usually be considered non-fragile.

- GRP: Heavyweight GRP sheets are available which satisfy the drop test independent of fixings. These can normally be considered non-fragile. Thinner and less stiff sheets are highly dependent on sheet type, profile, fixings and overlap. They should be considered fragile unless there is evidence that demonstrates otherwise.

- Steel: Steel liner sheets 0.4 mm thick or less should be considered fragile unless there is evidence that demonstrates otherwise.

- Fibre cement: These should normally be considered fragile unless there is evidence that demonstrates otherwise.

- All: All unfixed or temporarily fixed materials (irrespective of specification or type) should be treated as fragile until properly and fully fixed in accordance with the supplier's instructions. Only when they form a tested 'non-fragile' system can they be regarded as such.

Warning

The above list is not, and should not be seen as, definitive. It does not have a fully proven scientific basis. It does not mean that all the materials included in these broad categories are necessarily fragile or non-fragile. It does not take account of any of the other factors affecting fragility such as fixings. It is vital that those factors are taken into account.

Suppliers should state clearly the detailed configurations to which test data applies. They should indicate what that means in practice for both designers and installers in respect of ensuring safety.

APPENDIX 5 Demolition involving asbestos cement roof sheets

1   If the building contains any licensable asbestos (eg pipe insulation or sprayed coatings) **or** asbestos insulation board these materials should be removed **prior** to the rest of the demolition in accordance with the Asbestos Licensing regulations and the approprate Approved Code of Practice.[14]

2   There are two methods available to contractors intending to demolish structures of this type:

•   by hand;
•   by remote methods.

3   In order to choose the most suitable method, demolition contractors have to weigh up the following factors:

•   the exposure of the worker to asbestos dust;
•   contamination of the surrounding environment by asbestos dust;
•   the risk of falling, especially through the asbestos cement itself or roof lights.

Risk of exposure to and contamination by asbestos dust during work with asbestos cement

4   Asbestos cement is a grey, hard, brittle material normally containing 10-15% asbestos fibre. It is a dense material with a density greater than 1 tonne/m³. The asbestos fibres are tightly bound with cement. In order to release the asbestos fibres from asbestos cement the material needs to be crushed or ground into a fine dust. Activities such as sawing, drilling, wire brushing or crushing the material by tracking back and forth with heavy machinery are likely to produce dust containing asbestos fibres if the material is in a dry condition.

5   From the mid 1980s asbestos cement material contained only chrysotile (white asbestos) but prior to that crocidolite (blue asbestos) and amosite (brown asbestos) were used. Although all forms of asbestos can lead to the disease mesothelioma, the blue and brown forms are regarded as more of a hazard than white asbestos. The control limits for blue and brown asbestos laid down in the Control of Asbestos at Work Regulations are more stringent than for white asbestos. Although the majority of old asbestos cement sheets contain only white asbestos, contractors should establish whether or not there is any blue or brown asbestos present. If blue or brown asbestos is present, then the 'by hand' method may be more appropriate.

> **Second-hand asbestos cement sheet containing blue or brown asbestos cannot be resold. Regulation 4 of the Asbestos (Prohibitions) Regulations 1992 prohibits the supply of materials containing blue or brown asbestos.[14] Asbestos materials are 'special waste': your local Environment Agency area office will be able to advise on disposal.[9]**

Risk of falling

6   Many asbestos cement products, such as roof sheets, cladding, downpipes and gutters are located at height and therefore present a risk of falls. Asbestos cement sheet is a fragile material and cannot be relied upon to support the weight of a person. Over 50% of deaths in the construction industry are a result of falls, in particular from roofs and through fragile material such as asbestos cement sheets.

Demolition

Method 1 - by hand

7   If the asbestos cement sheets are in good condition and it is possible to provide safe access, preferably from underneath with access equipment such as scissor lifts, then the sheets should be taken down whole. When adopting this method the sheets should not be dropped or damaged. They are best disposed of by careful transfer to covered lorries or skips, or by wrapping intact in heavy duty sheet plastic.

Method 2 - remote

8   In some circumstances remote demolition by machine, such as a crane and a ball, pusher arm or deliberate controlled collapse is possible, for example if the sheets are in poor condition, ie liable to break when handled or safe access cannot be provided and the risk of falling is too great.

9   **Careful** remote demolition gives rise to low dust concentrations of about 0.1 f/ml, but subsequent clearance activities may result in a much higher concentration of more than 1 f/ml. To avoid the risk of the spread of contamination contractors should take the following precautions:

- Carry out and complete the work before demolition of the rest of the structure.
- Drop the material onto a clean, hard surface.
- Keep the material wet with gentle spraying.

- Remove waste and debris from the site as soon as possible to prevent it being disturbed, eg by moving vehicles. If material cannot be removed immediately, cover with heavy duty polythene.
- Take care to avoid plant being driven over asbestos cement sheet. Broken asbestos cement sheet if gathered by mechanical means should be well wetted to minimise fibre release. Broken asbestos cement sheet should not be bulldozed into a pile. Toothed buckets should not be used.
- Fine debris or waste liable to generate dust should be placed in suitable closed containers. Larger pieces of asbestos cement are best disposed of by careful transfer to covered lorries or skips.
- Containers (bags, skips etc) used for asbestos waste must be correctly labelled and disposed of to a licensed waste tip.[8]

Personal protective equipment

10   Masks suitable for working with asbestos should be worn if the control limits are liable to be exceeded, eg during subsequent clear up operations.[14] Workers should be provided with disposable overalls if dust is likely to be deposited on their clothes.

Concerns of the public

11   To members of the public the remote method appears noisy, dusty and often uncontrolled. They are often concerned about demolition of this type when they know or suspect the building was roofed or clad with asbestos cement. In order to alleviate these concerns about this type of work contractors are advised to:

- keep the neighbours informed about the work;
- consult the local environmental health department.

APPENDIX 6   Safe operation of bitumen boilers

1   Bitumen boilers are widely used in work on flat roofs. Two types of risk need to be controlled:

- fire and explosion risk from storage and use of liquid petroleum gas (LPG);
- contact with hot bitumen.

2   Providing the right equipment, keeping it in good condition and training workers in basic good practice will help to reduce accidents to workers and the public.

3   When setting up the boiler, a number of basic safety guidelines should be followed:

- Stand the boiler on a firm level surface which should be non-combustible and capable of carrying the load.
- Set up the gas cylinders at least 3 m away from the boiler unless a suitable protective shield is fitted.
- Do not have more cylinders than you need for that day's work: additional cylinders should be stored safely.
- Make sure that hoses are of the correct type, are in good condition and properly connected.
- Check for leaks before use: soapy water is ideal - **never** use a naked flame.
- Do not smoke or allow others to smoke.
- Have at least one fire extinguisher close by (9 L foam or 9 kg dry powder).
- Never leave the boiler unattended when lit or hot.
- Protect with suitable barriers where other workers or the public may have access.
- Unless they are safe by location, remove the gas cylinders when the boiler is not in use to prevent unauthorised use or interference.
- Keep other combustibles such as paper, packaging, etc, well away.

4   While heating the bitumen:

- Follow the maker's instructions on lighting up.
- Do not exceed the recommended operating temperature for the particular grade of bitumen used.
- When heating from cold, keep heating rates low until the bitumen is clearly liquid and any water has been driven off.
- Add bitumen carefully - avoid splashing.
- Gas fired bitumen heating boilers should **never** be used for heating cut-back bitumens. These contain solvents which can be easily ignited by such open-flame heating and a rapidly escalating fire would ensue.

5   Precautions during use:

*   Keep water away from hot bitumen.
*   Never use a ladle to remove bitumen: use the draw off tap.
*   Wear suitable eye protection, foot protection and gloves.
*   Wear suitable clothing to avoid skin contact from splashes.
*   Do not heat the bitumen drums unless they are designed for that purpose.
*   Keep the lid on the boiler as much as possible.
*   Regularly check the boiler temperature and level.
*   Carry bitumen in proper containers, eg lidded buckets.
*   Have a clear, safe route from the boiler to where the bitumen is used.
*   Ensure that lifting equipment used, eg pulleys, blocks ropes etc is suitable and in good condition, before and after each job. See paragraphs 26-33 above and the section on 'small lifting equipment' in HSE's publication *Health and safety in construction* HSG150.[1]

6   After use:

*   Turn off the gas at the cylinders.
*   Prevent build-up of bitumen on the outside of the boiler by regular removal of drips and splashes. Excessive spillages should be dealt with promptly.

7   At all times:

*   Make sure the boiler does not overheat or run low.
*   Turn the gas off before leaving the boiler unattended, even for a short time.
*   Never apply direct heat to pipes or valves, or to the outside of the boiler.
*   Turn off the burner before towing the boiler on a lorry or trailer.
*   Follow general advice on safe storage and use of LPG.[24]

8   Workers and supervisers should be trained in first aid procedures for bitumen burns. This should be confirmed by written instructions clearly available on site. Further information is given in an industry code of practice for the safe operation of propane fired bitumen boilers.[26]

Acknowledgements

Briggs Roofing Ltd

Carehaven Ltd

Coxdome Ltd

Facelift Access Hire

Homebase Ltd

Llewellyn Construction Ltd

National Federation of Roofing Contractors

Plettac NSG

Rossway Dowd Ltd

Safesite Ltd

SGB

Trussed Rafters Association

Trusswal Twinaplate Ltd

Higher Safety Ltd

References and further reading

References

1   *Health and safety in construction* HSG150 HSE Books 1996 ISBN 0 7176 1143 4

2   *Fire safety in construction work* HSG168 HSE Books 1997 ISBN 0 7176 1332 1

3   *Code of practice for safe use of cranes. Part 1 General* BS 7121: Part 1 1989

4   *Safe use of work equipment Provision and Use of Work Equipment Regulations 1998* L22 HSE Books 1998 ISBN 0 7176 1626 6

5   *Work in windy conditions* Available from: National Federation of Roofing Contractors Publications Ltd, 24 Weymouth Street, London WIN 4LX

6   *Electrical safety on construction sites* HSG141 HSE Books 1995 ISBN 0 7176 1000 4

7   *Code of practice for distribution of electricity on construction and building sites* BS 7375: 1996

8   *Special Waste Regulations 1996 The controls on special waste: how they affect you* EP147 Environment Agency 1996

9   *Protecting the public - your next move* HSG151 HSE Books 1997 ISBN 0 7176 1148 5

10   *Codes of practice for slating and tiling. Part 1 Design* BS 5534: Part 1 1997

11   *Trussed rafter association technical handbook 1997* Available from: Trussed Rafter
        Association, 41 Bowles Hill, Rowlands Castle, Hampshire PO9 6BP

12   *Safety signs and signals: The Health and Safety (Safety Signs and Signals) Regulations 1996
        Guidance on Regulations* L64 HSE Books 1997 ISBN 0 7176 0870 0

13   *A step by step guide to COSHH assessment* HSG97 HSE Books 1998 ISBN 0 7176 1446 8

14   *The control of asbestos at work: Control of Asbestos at Work Regulations 1987
        Approved Code of Practice* L27 HSE Books 1993 ISBN 0 11 882037 0

15   *Control of Lead at Work Regulations 1998 Approved Code of Practice, Regulations and
        guidance* COP2 HSE Books 1998 ISBN 0 7176 1506 5

16   *Health risk management: a practical guide for managers in small and medium-sized enterprises*
        HSG137 HSE Books 1995 ISBN 0 7176 0905 7

17   *Working with asbestos cement and asbestos insulating board* EH71 HSE Books 1996
        ISBN 0 7176 1247 3

18   *EH40/98 Occupational exposure limits 1998* HSE Books 1998 ISBN 0 7176 1474 3

19   *Keep your top on* INDG147(rev) HSE Books 1998

20   *Safety nets. Part 1 Safety requirements test method* EN 1263: Part 1 1997

21   *Safety nets. Part 2 Safety requirements for erection of safety nets* EN 1263: Part 2 1998

22   *Code of practice for use of safety nets, containment nets and sheets on constructional works*
        BS 8093: 1991

23   *Guidelines on the use of rope access methods for industrial purposes*
        Industrial Rope Access Trade Association 1997 ISBN 0 9523227 14

24   *Storage of full and empty LPG cylinders and cartridges Code of Practice 7* LP Gas Association 1998

25   *Workplace (Health, Safety and Welfare) Regulations 1992 Approved Code of Practice*
        L24 HSE Books 1992 ISBN 0 7176 0413 6

26   *Containers attached to mobile gas-fired equipment Code of Practice No 10*
        LP Gas Association 1998

Further reading

Management of Health and Safety at Work Regulations 1992 Approved code of practice L21
HSE Books 1992 ISBN 0 7176 0412 8

5 steps to risk assessment INDG163(rev1) HSE Books 1998

A guide to risk assessment requirements INDG218

A guide to Construction (Health Safety and Welfare) Regulations 1996 INDG220 HSE Books 1996

A guide to managing health and safety in construction HSE Books 1995 ISBN 0 7176 0755 0

Designing for health and safety in construction HSE Books 1995 ISBN 0 7176 0807 7

CDM Regulations, work sector guidance for designers CIRIA Report 166 ISBN 0 86017 464 6
Available from CIRIA, 6 Storey's Gate, Westminster, London SW1P 3AU

Successful health and safety management HSG65 HSE Books 1997 ISBN 0 7176 1276 7

Asbestos materials in buildings HMSO 1991 ISBN 0 11 752370 4

Inclined hoists used in building and construction work PM63 HSE Books 1987 ISBN 0 11 883945 4

Managing asbestos in workplace buildings INDG223(rev1) HSE Books 1996

Site safe news Available from SRJ Units 3 and 5-9, Grain Industrial Estate, Harlow Street,
Liverpool L8 4XY, Tel: 0151 709 1354

The future availability and accuracy of the references listed in this publication cannot be
guaranteed.

Printed and published by the Health and Safety Executive

C30   4/04